THE GOURMET ROTATION DIET FOR ALLERGY SUFFERERS

THE GOURMET ROTATION DIET FOR ALLERGY SUFFERERS

By

Joyce Weaver

With foreword by Dr Honor Anthony

Date of Publication:
2002

Published by:
Joyce Weaver

Printed by:
ProPrint
Riverside Cottage
Great North Road
Stibbington
Peterborough PE8 6LR

ISBN: 0-9543944-0-2

ACKNOWLEDGEMENTS

My heartfelt thanks to all the doctors who have helped us over the years.
Our wonderful GP Dr Roger Kaufmann for his support and understanding.
Dr Kate Ward and her Dietician Angela Freeman for treating Peter, you both did a brilliant job!
To Dr Damien Downing for all his support and my medical treatment which has made such a dramatic difference to my health.
To Dr Jonathan Maberly and Dr Honor Anthony for all the amazing work they've done at Airedale Allergy Centre not just for Howard but all the countless other patients over the years who found it impossible to get effective treatment elsewhere. On behalf of all the patients at the Airedale Allergy Centre I would also like to offer thanks to Dr Econs for taking over the outpatients clinic and continuing the good work there.
To Mrs Elaine Maberly and Angela Freeman for all their advice and help. Especially, I would like to offer my thanks to Dr Honor Anthony for reading through my manuscript and for all her patience, guidance and support.
Lastly I would like to thank my husband Howard for his help with the book and Peter and David for just being there for me and spurring me on when I felt like giving up.
My love to you all and God Bless.

Joyce Weaver

In Loving Memory
of
My dear Mother Evelyn

FOREWORD

Our forebears mostly ate foods that were in season, using simple preservatives to store the excess to help them through the winter. In the last fifty years modern food technology has increasingly allowed and encouraged us to eat the same food constituents every day, brought to us from all over the world, possibly because of the availability of chemical food preservatives. Much of the modern diet is now composed of pre-prepared labour-saving meals containing too much sugar and fat, disguised by artificial colouring and flavouring. Chemicals used in manufacturing processes may be present as well as other contaminants from intensive agriculture. Hidden food allergy was recognised as a cause of chronic illness in the USA in the 1920s, and it has been increasing throughout the developed world in the last fifty years, becoming very common. It may give rise to a wide range of symptoms, which often vary in severity from day to day although the links with the provoking foods are rarely obvious and usually missed.

Are these facts connected? Probably. The same chronic ills are spreading to developing countries as their use of synthetic chemicals increases and they adopt our food habits. Moreover in practice, when hidden food allergy is investigated, the main culprits are usually those foods which the patient has been eating very frequently. Rotation diets help to re-establish tolerance.

In a strict four-day rotation diet, the same food is only eaten once in every four days, and each food family is restricted to one of the four days. This is an important tool in helping patients with severe problems to shake off their intolerance and can be more generally useful in trying to reduce chronic ills. Although the diets individually designed for each patient by an experienced allergy clinic are usually healthier and better balanced than the diets which the patients were eating previously, in most cook's hands a four-day rotation diet results in a rather dull menu with a very limited range of options for each day. Joyce Weaver has shown that this need not be the case. She bases her approach to this challenge on her family's experience and her training in food technology and has produced a wide range of recipes based on a slightly relaxed four-day rotation. It will, of course, have to be interpreted with discretion by some patients according to which foods they are having to avoid, if necessary moving foods from one day to another in order to make sure that each day has adequate sources of the important groups of foods - filling foods, proteins, and vegetables or fruits. If in doubt they should consult a dietician. Keeping the food families to a single day is important only for a minority of patients; adequate nutrition is essential for all. Since being ill often increases the need for vitamins and minerals, taking a wide-range hypoallergenic supplement in addition is a wise move for many: most people who are rotating should at least take a calcium and magnesium supplement on their non-milk days.

The book should also improve the lot of the families of patients with food intolerances, especially those members who do the meal planning and cooking. Presented with the exciting recipes she describes, the families may not even be aware that their foods are being rotated.

Dr Honor Anthony
Specialist in Allergy and Environmental Medicine
Adel, Leeds.

Dr Anthony was associated with the Airedale Allergy Centre for many years, - this was the first purpose-built environmentally-controlled inpatient unit in the world. She is co-author of the text Environmental Medicine in Clinical Practice by Anthony, Birtwistle, Eaton and Maberly, IBSN 0 9523397 2 2 available from BSAENM Publications Tel 02380 812124.

CONTENTS

INTRODUCTION

This is a book of recipes for tasty and satisfying dishes, but with a difference. They are recipes designed to help people with food allergy and intolerance to have more interesting meals and to recover their health more quickly. They may also help to reduce the risk of allergies for the whole family. They have helped my family; I hope they will help yours too.

As our family knows to its cost, allergies are becoming more common, both between children and adults. Food allergy and intolerance can cause many different conditions - Asthma, Migraine and chronic headaches, Eczema, Rhinitis, Urticaria, Angioneurotic Oedema, Hyperkinetic Syndrome, Irritable Bowel Syndrome, food induced psychological states such as depression and anxiety, and other symptoms such as aching limbs and chronic fatigue.

Some experts believe that all the chemicals we eat and inhale may be part of the cause but that it is made worse by the fact that we eat a relatively small number of foods, served up in a variety of different ways, but mostly containing the same ingredients all the year round. There are far more foods available, and this book will show you how to use them to prepare really varied dishes.

One of the problems many sufferers face is the question: 'What on earth can I eat today?' People with food intolerances tend to stick to the same few 'safe foods' to which they may eventually become sensitised, if they eat them on a daily basis, and so their diet becomes even more restricted. By rotating and varying your diet as much as possible you are obtaining a wider spectrum of nutrients and allowing your body to lose some of its sensitivity to certain foods to which you have acquired an intolerance. Although I should make it clear at this point that any allergies you were born with, for instance peanut allergy, are fixed allergies and you will always have to avoid these.

Food rotation diets are not a new concept. It is many years now since Dr Theron Randolph first introduced his Rotation Diet which he developed for his patients in America.

Dr Richard Mackarness (in the UK) developed the Stone Age diet. Dr Honor Anthony, Dr Maberly and staff at the Airedale

Allergy Centre developed their own rotation version of this diet. My husband was advised to use it for a while before being admitted as an in-patient at Airedale Allergy Centre. Since his treatment there and my own treatment at a clinic in York, we have devised our own expanded version of this diet to give sufferers as much choice and variety as possible to allow for likes and dislikes, existing food allergies and intolerances.

I should point out that for the first few days of using this diet plan you may feel a great deal worse as you suffer withdrawal symptoms to your favourite 'fixes'. You will probably find it easier to allow four separate cupboards for each day's staple foods so that you don't get them mixed up. Colour coded stickers are a big help too, as is a four tier vegetable rack and four separate freezer compartments. This all sounds complicated on the outset but I can assure you that the benefits you gain in restored health and vitality are well worth the initial effort of setting up the diet.

You will probably find it easier to divide your shopping list into four short lists instead of one long one.

You will also find it beneficial to make charts and record what you have eaten on a daily basis so that you can then note down any unpleasant reactions to foods. This is fairly straightforward when you are only eating foods on a minimum 4 day cycle and it becomes much easier to identify the foods which are giving you problems. Once your problem foods have been identified you may feel able to relax the four day rotation within reason, depending on how severe your symptoms are.

Although for the most part all members of the same food family are on the same day, the grass family has been split on to two alternate days because otherwise you would have one day without any complex carbohydrates to keep up your calorie intake. All the members containing gluten are on day one and the others, maize, rice and wild rice are on day three. If you have problems finding enough foods that agree with you on a particular day, you may have to eat some from an alternate day to make up the calories. For instance if you react to the nightshade family on day four you may have to eat other vegetables from day two.

I know how difficult it can be to find specialist treatment for allergies. My family and I have been very lucky to have such a kind and supportive GP who has always been prepared to listen to my views and convictions with patience and understanding without ever dismissing my theories out of hand and making me feel silly. I know only too well that without his support my family's story could have been very different.

The British Society for Allergy, Environmental and Nutritional Medicine are willing to supply you with a list of specialist doctors who practise nutritional medicine, if you send an SAE. The address is given at the back of the book along with their list of publications which your doctor may find helpful.

Very few doctors in general practice have any in-depth knowledge of the wider implications of allergies on our health, and I feel that the more people who ask for this specialised kind of help, get the right treatment, and benefit from it, the better that understanding will be for everyone.

Joyce Weaver

CHAPTER ONE

MY FAMILY'S STORY

I have no medical qualifications to advise anyone about allergies and their effect on our health, but I do have a great deal of personal and often painful experience of the subject. My husband Howard, our eldest son Peter and myself are all chronic allergy sufferers and it was only through flashes of intuition, the patience and kind support of our GP, and of course, the skill of our respective allergy specialists, that we have, by stages, got to the roots of our health problems.

I believe that our son Peter's health problems began whilst he was still in the womb. At the time I was expecting him, I was working as a baker and confectioner in a small family business in Retford, North Nottinghamshire.

It was 1977, the year of the Queen's Silver Jubilee. I was five months pregnant when the orders started rolling in for special gateaux with red, white and blue rosettes made of modelling paste. The colouring was kneaded into the paste by hand and my hands and fingernails were stained a deep navy blue and lurid red. The stains took nearly three weeks to fade and I am ashamed to say that I was greedy enough and stupid enough to eat the gaudily coloured scraps of modelling paste. This was not an isolated incident, I regularly decorated cakes and quite often got my hands stained with food colouring and nibbled on the scraps of paste which were left over without ever giving it a thought.

A children's allergy specialist told me several years later that such high concentration's of food colourings were probably absorbed into my bloodstream and would have crossed the placental barrier, along with my antibodies, in effect, Peter was sensitised before he was born. There were other things too that I ate on a daily basis thinking that they were good for me and my baby. We made egg custards with eggs bought from the local supermarket, I had at least one a day. I never gave any thought to the 'egg colour' (Tartrazine) that went into the pastry or for that matter what went into the eggs via the feed the hens were given, it wasn't until Peter was a few months old that I suspected the truth.

After Peter was born, he was a very 'windy' baby. He never settled down to sleep for very long. He suffered dreadfully with nappy rash and certain types of washing powder and scented baby cleansers seemed to aggravate the problem. I was breastfeeding him and advised by the district nurse to drink plenty of fluids such as lemon barley water and dilute orange squash or lucozade. I'd stopped drinking coffee when I became pregnant because it made me feel sick and I'd never drunk tea for the same reason, so dilute squashes seemed like a good idea at the time. I had no idea that traces of colouring and preservatives were getting into my breastmilk. Looking back, there's no wonder the poor child had problems sleeping.

When he did manage to sleep, he would often wake with a start and begin crying and drawing his knees up to his chest, racked with stomach-ache. We got through gripe water like it was going out of fashion, but the relief never seemed to last for very long. I sought advice from the local baby clinic only to be informed that 'all babies love to yell dear and anyway it's good for their lungs.'

Our problems began in earnest when Peter was three months old. He'd started teething so I had decided to put him on the bottle, I'd had to supplement his feeds with formula milk for a while anyway so it was relatively easy to wean him. The trouble was that his teeth were pressing through blood vessels in his gums and it hurt him to feed. I was advised by the nurse at the clinic to rub Dentinox on his gums and to clean his new teeth with strawberry flavoured toothpaste. Neither of us were concerned that both of these products contained food colourings. In 1977 people were blissfully ignorant of the health and behaviour problems caused by azo dyes, (which are additives such as food colourings) and preservatives. Maurice Hanssen and Jill Marsden hadn't then written 'E for Additives' and raised public awareness of allergy problems and so, as it was, Peter's stomach cramps got worse.

The family doctor said it was probably three month colic. I pointed out to him that Peter had been like this ever since he was born, but that he seemed to be getting worse. The doctor prescribed

Infant Gaviscon to be taken before each feed. It helped for a while but didn't get to the root of the problem.

Our local health visitor called and suggested he should be trying different foods each day, such as unsalted mashed potato, banana, baby rice and soft boiled eggs. (Nowadays a paediatric dietician would probably not recommend trying a baby with eggs until the child was at least nine months old). Peter was fine with the first three foods, but when I gave him a soft boiled egg to try, some of it dribbled down his chin and he gulped it down with a shudder. He began to cry and was violently sick. I was horrified to see that everywhere the egg had dribbled on his chin there were huge blisters. He looked as though he'd been scaled. I bundled him into his pram and rushed down to the clinic. The nurse on duty advised me not to give him egg again for a few weeks as he'd had an allergic reaction to it.

I stared dumbly at a poster on the wall behind her. It was a colourful parody of a woman whose face and body were made up of a variety of fruits and vegetables, cream cakes and hamburgers. Underneath was the stark message 'You are what you eat.' I have found out over the years that this is only partly true, the message should be, 'You are what you eat, drink and breathe.'

I waited several weeks before trying Peter with egg again but when I did his reaction was the same, blistered skin, projectile vomiting and crying unconsolably.

One day Peter and I paid an unexpected visit to my parents. They wanted us to stay for lunch but all they had to offer Peter were homemade baps cut into soldiers, still warm from the oven, and some free range bantam eggs from a local smallholding. These were genuinely free range from bantam hens that were fed on corn and grits, bran mash and the odd juicy worm or two that they found as they wandered around the yard. I was reluctant to let my mother give them to Peter to say the least, but I was astounded to see him devour two bantam eggs with obvious enjoyment. Even though the egg white dribbled down his chin, there was no blistering not even slight redness! I felt elated as we went home on the bus.

A few days later I tried him again with eggs from the local supermarket. Within seconds of eating it, the skin was blistering on his chin and he was violently sick before bursting into tears. That was the last time I ever bought eggs from there to give to my son. I have since learnt that animal feed merchants take colour charts with them when they visit egg producers so that they can choose what shade of yellow they want the yolk to be, they then include additives to the feed and mix it accordingly.

When Peter was two and a half years old we moved to North Yorkshire. We'd brought with us an old sheepskin hearth rug which Peter began to use as a sort of comfort blanket. He loved to curl up on it in front of the fire and go to sleep. He probably found that it reminded him of his first home and his first friends and so we just went along with him. Peter had also just been given a feather pillow and feather quilt by his grandad, 'To keep him cosy and warm.' Neither Howard nor myself had ever heard of house dust mites or the devastating effects that they could have on your health, once you became sensitised to them. It was several years before we finally got to the root causes of Peter's health problems.

When he started school, the wheezy chest he'd had for a while became much worse. He was taunted and bullied because he'd developed a squint and needed glasses and eye patches. He was often weepy and miserable with a constant runny nose and watery eyes. He would regularly wake up in the night crying with pains in his legs for no apparent reason. The doctor we had at the time thought they might be growing pains but they always coincided with his wheezy chest which was eventually diagnosed as asthma. He also developed eczema on the insides of his elbows and the backs of his knees. On several occasions when we had to call out the doctor, Peter's asthma was so bad he would slip into unconsciousness and delirium. Our GP thought he probably had a re-occurring flu virus for his symptoms to be so severe and prescribed antibiotics to no avail. I was worried sick. My sister Sheila died of asthma at five and a half years of age. His attacks would often start with temper tantrums, flushed cheeks, vomiting or a hacking cough, then wheezing, loss of consciousness and delirium.

One of Howard's work colleagues saw an article in a newspaper about the work of two allergy specialists, one of whom is a paediatrician, who were both based at Airedale General Hospital near Keighley, West Yorkshire. By now we'd moved house again and our new GP was very supportive and understanding and he managed to get Peter referred to the paediatric allergy specialist. We were amazed to find her office piled high with case files on children with allergy problems of various sorts. She cheerfully informed us that only the previous day a small boy, who'd been as good as gold all morning, was given a banana as a 'challenge food' and within less than ten minutes of eating it had gone totally berserk and literally set about wrecking her office. He'd thrown all her files on the floor, and then began tossing papers everywhere, before jumping all over her desk. She and the dietician had spent hours sorting things out again.

The doctor put Peter on an exclusion diet and we had to re-introduce one food at a time. Interestingly, whilst on the exclusion diet, which consisted of Rice Krispies with 7up on, lamb, potatoes, carrots, celery and pears for dessert, with gluten free bread and biscuits, Ketovite vitamin and mineral supplements and not much else. Peter actually put on nearly three quarters of a stone in weight. (He'd always been painfully thin, despite having a good appetite).

It was a slow and painstaking process. We had to make charts and write down everything he ate and drank and note down his reaction. It took the best part of six months to find out all his allergies. He was allergic to: house dust mites, feathers, food colourings, preservatives, ie (sodium metabisulphite, sodium benzoate, benzoic acid, potassium benzoate and sulphur dioxide), antioxidants, ie (Butylated Hydroxyanisole and Butylated Hydroxytoluene) artificial sweeteners, ie (aspartame, asculfame and saccharin), artificial flavourings which contained sodium benzoate as the preservative (although he could tolerate those which were preserved with isopropyl alcohol) milk and dairy products, eggs, tea and coffee and cigarette smoke, (very severe reaction to this).

Both the specialist and her dietician were very kind and supportive and stressed that if we had any problems we should ring them straight away. I was amazed at their vast knowledge of food additives and painfully aware that my own knowledge of the subject (gained on a four year City & Guilds Course,) was nearly twenty years out of date.

At the end of the six month period, Peter's rhinitis had cleared up. As well as changes to his diet, we'd changed his feather quilt and pillow for some dustmite proof bedding, developed especially for allergy sufferers. He had a mattress cover to seal in the dust mites and new lino on the floor instead of carpet. I damp dusted every day and we bought an air cleaner. The pains in his legs disappeared, as did the eczema and his squint and he doesn't need glasses anymore.

Now several years later, my wheezy little invalid, who could barely swim a length at our local baths, is a strapping six feet two inches tall and he can easily swim thirty lengths straight off, although he complains that the chlorinated water makes his nose run.

He now has lots of friends and only needs his inhaler if he goes into a smoky pub. It's years since he had a severe asthma attack, thank goodness.

I'm thankful that David, our younger son, doesn't suffer from allergies to any serious extent. He is three and a half years younger than Peter and I took great care when I was expecting him not to eat or drink any of the things that I knew had sensitised Peter. David has always been a placid boy. He's quiet, thoughtful, and intelligent with a wonderful sense of humour. He rarely gets colds or flu and is a popular lad with a wide circle of friends. He even manages to be popular with his course tutors!

I must stress at this point that under no circumstances should a parent attempt to try an exclusion diet on their child without support from their doctor and referral through him to a children's allergy specialist who is working closely with a qualified dietician with a deep understanding of allergy problems in children.

* * * * * *

My husband Howard's story is in some ways similar to Peter's. And I will let him tell it himself.

As a little boy I'd had a squint which three operations only made worse.

Even as a small child I'd begun to realise that certain foods, such as eggs, disagreed with me and the smell of my mother's perfume and cigarettes made me ill.

As I grew up my body was getting regular exposure to cigarette smoke from family and friends and regular exposure to volatile organic chemicals through my first job in a chemical company laboratory. I suffered dermatitis on contact with certain chemicals.

In my early twenties my life was shaped when I met Joyce, my co-author and wife. I was living in a bachelor flat, cooking for myself as my parents had bought a shop and moved to another district.

In my twenties I went through good times of getting married and bad times as Mum developed Multiple Sclerosis, which eventually killed her.

Joyce and I were highly stressed as we moved in with Mum and Dad to help them with their business. I was now working full time in a paper mill. There was less exposure to chemicals but exposure to heat, noise, lots of tea and coffee, and lots of cigarette smoke.

After Mum's death, the business was sold and we bought our first married home. Stress continued at work until one day, after lunch, I collapsed with severe stomach pains and heat exhaustion and I was rushed into hospital. The doctors could not find anything wrong and after a few days I was back at work.

This episode did not stop me from changing jobs back to my first chemical industry employer, in a junior management position. Fortunately, there was little exposure to chemicals, but the job did bring exposure to stress, cigarette smoke, travel and exhaust fumes.

Two houses moves and two children later, I was smitten with a form of glandular fever. Foolishly, I decided to work on. Very, very slowly, after weeks and months, my health seemed to get better, but I was getting severe headaches on Saturdays, when we regularly bought Chinese take away meals after our weekend shopping trips. Mono Sodium Glutamate is a common ingredient in Chinese restaurants, and take away cuisine, and many people react to it, although I didn't know it at the time, I also got severe nausea after eating jam and bread. My reaction was to cut wheat out of my diet, which seemed to make me better.

Soon after this, Dad died. I went through a bad patch and my weight dropped. Eventually I got back to what seemed normal. To boost my health, I took the kids swimming quite often and regularly exposed myself to chlorine. Memories came back of occasional severe stomach pains, discomfort in the back passage and frequent trips to the toilet in the night

Things came to a head on a business trip to South Africa in 1993. On the way there I noticed a mouth abscess which I dismissed as an ulcer. A combination of heat, stress, chlorine, from the hotel swimming pool, tiredness and the wrong food hit me. I was rushed to hospital with excruciating stomach pain and nausea, (still not knowing what was wrong or that I had severe allergies). After three days of being starved and rehydrated I was OK to travel home, but remained in a bad way until the abscess was removed and then rallied. Investigation at my local hospital did not reveal anything. Joyce's strong suspicion that the cause was allergies was dismissed by the specialist. Although he agreed to do a 'RAST' test which proved negative.

Having rallied, a holiday at the seaside was just the tonic we needed. Great Yarmouth proved less beneficial than we'd hoped. Acute stomach pains and nausea started all over again and I was rushed into hospital. As before, nothing was organically wrong and after starvation and re-hydration I was OK.

I started keeping a diary of my symptoms and experimented with my diet. Hardly a day went by without me having problems. No foods agreed with me. My legs swelled up after Christmas and my weight was dropping. Thankfully, at Joyce's insistence, I was referred to an allergy specialist, (who was at that time based at Airedale General Hospital, where our son Peter went for his treatment). It was actually his colleague who saw me. She has written many papers about allergies, and is a leading expert in her own right. After a two hour consultation I was so emotional. She believed me and confirmed that I did have severe food allergies. I needed urgent medical treatment and advised that I should go on the

'Stone Age Diet' immediately. She also said I should be admitted to Airedale Allergy Centre as an in-patient as soon as possible.

It became obvious that the NHS was not going to finance the treatment. Fortunately, an angel came to my rescue and I got quick attention.

I had no idea what to expect. The treatment was extreme. Starvation for four days, (It should have been five but I was too weak). Testing of chemicals, inhalants and tap water. I was allergic to most things, including tap water! (I had drunk lots of tap water for years). Then the food testing starting. The one that really stays in the mind was the test for beetroot (simulating beet sugar). The stomach pain was unbearable. I pleaded for morphine. It was not possible to give it to me, somehow, I got through it and found my most potent enemy. During my three weeks stay, another thirty six food enemies were identified. It would be nigh on impossible to live without the thirty seven foods. Fortunately the treatment included the development of a Specific Neutralising Vaccine which literally switches off the allergic reaction and allows me to eat all the foods on a four day rotation. A separate vaccine protects me against chlorine and cigarette fumes. A third vaccine protects me against moulds and spores.

Perhaps even more important, the treatment has taught me about myself, my body and how to live a healthy active life. It also taught me that my experience could help others. I have found that allergies, eczema, migraine, asthma and other symptoms can be related. They can be caused by food allergy, food intolerance, chemical intolerance, and environmental factors. On returning home it was time to practice what the doctors and their staff preached.

Little things changed first. Bleach was banned. Perfumes were removed. Simple Soap, fragrance free shampoos and expensive unperfumed washing powder were adopted. Joyce filtered the air in the house with an air cleaner and the kitchen cooker hood. The next step was to hot wash the pillows and duvet at the launderette, (this was stressful as the launderette was full of cigarette smoke). We got dust mite proof mattress and pillow covers. (Available at many leading high street stores).

Having done all the simple things, we moved on to more expensive items - A plumbed in water filter, (from the recommended list of suppliers issued by the clinic). A dehumidifier with air filter. (This reduces the dustmite, mould and spore populations in the house). Later we bought a vacuum cleaner which was developed especially for allergy sufferers and was again from a list of recommended ones from the allergy centre, (we have not included vacuum cleaners in the list of useful suppliers at the end of the book because technology is improving all the time and there are now a great many vacuum cleaners fitted with HEPA filters to aid allergy sufferers).

Of course as well as environment, diet became a major consideration. I had to follow the four day rotation devised for me at Airedale and also introduce new foods. It was stressed that oily fish would be beneficial to me. My specific neutralising vaccines were taken as recommended and I started to improve.

I have never been rushed into hospital since and have only had one serious bout of pain requiring morphine from the doctor. That was brought about by intense stress at work and happened nearly three years ago. I look after myself and still follow the rotation. I take one daily multivitamin and mineral tablet, three 1000mg Evening Primrose Oil capsules and two Cod Liver Oil capsules daily.

Since my time at the clinic, I have not had one day off work through illness. My weight is around thirteen stones in contrast to just about ten and a half stones after Airedale. My quality of life is much better and all the credit must go to Airedale Allergy Centre.

Joyce takes up the story again-

I think my own allergy problems had been creeping up on me for years. When I became pregnant with Peter, I suddenly found that I couldn't bear the taste of coffee and that the smell of it made me feel sick, (as did broad beans and fried onions). I'd never been a tea drinker. As a child it used to make me feel sick, but I'd always loved the taste of coffee, even though it gave me stomach-ache.

As I grew older I suppose I must have developed a tolerance for it, but when I became pregnant that tolerance broke down and my system rebelled. I didn't drink coffee much until several years later. After David was born, people would invite me round for coffee with the kids and it seemed rude not to accept, so I began drinking it again. Soon I was hooked on caffeine and drinking it by the gallon. I began to suffer blinding migraine headaches that lasted up to ten days, at a time. I would be permanently exhausted, irritable and depressed. The only thing that seemed to give me any relief was my next cup of coffee, my next fix! I tried Migraleve, Codeine and even the Distalgesics I'd been prescribed for a slipped disc but nothing seemed to work. In addition to the migraines, I'd developed pains down my neck and shoulders and into my arms. My hands were aching and tingling with pins and needles. It was soon after I'd realized that Peter was allergic to colouring and preservatives that I decided to take stock of my own health problems. I didn't need to be a genius to recognise that my headaches had started when I re-introduced coffee into my diet, so I tried switching to decaffeinated but I felt just as bad, so stopped drinking it altogether. My migraines dissipated, but I still felt tired and drained a lot of the time and had difficulty concentrating on anything for very long. I suffered a lot with headache and pains down my sciatic nerves, which I assumed were caused by the disc injury I'd incurred a few years earlier. I spent a fortune at the local osteopath's trying to put it right. To cut a long story short, whilst Howard was in Airedale Allergy Clinic, he discussed my health problems with the doctor there who recommended that I should be referred to a clinic in York.

On my first visit to the York clinic, I had to fill in a questionnaire, listing all my symptoms and any foods which I already know I was sensitive to. The doctor explained this would save time during the first consultation and that he had to be sure I really was an allergy sufferer before he would commit me to long term treatment which may not have been appropriate for me. This way, I would not be wasting his time and my money.

He recommended that I had a cytotoxic test, (a form of blood test) to determine the full extent of my allergy problems, followed later by an Enzyme Potentiated Desensitisation injection, EPD for short. (See appendix).

I was shocked when I received my own test results in the post the morning after my blood test. The list was three pages long and the results were numbered, 0 = no reaction, 1 = mild reaction, 2 = moderate reaction, 3 = severe reaction.

I was severely allergic to white flour, eggs, milk and dairy products, citrus fruits and berries such as raspberries, blackberries, etc. yeast, haricot beans, tomatoes, hazelnuts, tea and coffee and moderately allergic to chlorine, housedust mites, car exhaust fumes, mould spores, chocolate etc.

I had another consultation with the doctor to discuss my results and have my first EPD.

He advised me to avoid all the foods on my severe list and to rotate all the other foods on a four day basis. (By this time Howard and I had already worked out a four day rotation diet for him to follow after his treatment at Airedale Allergy Centre, roughly based on the Stone Age Diet, and so it was relatively easy for me to adapt it for my own needs). Once we'd got the instructions for my diet sorted out it was time for my EPD.

This was administered as an intradermal injection. In this, the needle was introduced in between the layers of skin on my forearm, to produce a weal which looked rather like a large insect bite. Indeed it certainly felt like a bee sting for the first few seconds. However the pain quickly subsided and I was sent back to the waiting room for ten minutes, just to make sure the EPD had taken properly.

I have to say that after my first one, I was spark out on the sofa for three days with a thumping headache and I felt totally exhausted and unable to think clearly but soon after that I began to experience a vitality and mental clarity I hadn't had for a long time. I stripped and redecorated our bedroom and gave the house a spring clean from top to bottom. But by degrees, my new found energy began to tail off and I was well ready for my next injection six weeks later.

I now have an EPD once every six months, which will eventually stretch to once a year. I can truthfully say I feel much better, although I do still get headaches occasionally, especially if I get exposed to cigarette smoke, which I've always had difficulty coping with. (EPD cannot desensitise a person to this unfortunately).

At one time a trip to a city such as Leeds would leave me totally exhausted for two or three days, mainly due to air pollution, but the doctor discovered that my liver wasn't working properly and was failing to produce the enzyme needed to break down sulphites into harmless sulphates. This caused fluid retention among other things. I was put on a course of tablets to stimulate my liver into making the necessary enzyme, and hypoallergenic multivitamin supplements, for around eighteen months before the problem was rectified. I still have problems with cigarette smoke and traffic fumes but to nowhere near the same degree, thank goodness. I still take the hypoallergenic vitamin and mineral supplements every day and they help a great deal. I'm not chronically tired anymore, and I feel generally able to cope with life. Until recently I worked full-time in an office in Leeds, something that I would never have contemplated a few years ago, and I could happily delve into the basement archives, (which date back to 1947 and are quite musty) without any reaction to the clouds of dust which at one time would have left me feeling ill for days!

CHAPTER TWO

HINTS & TIPS

It's virtually impossible to devise a recipe book to suit all allergy sufferers. We are all individuals and so our needs will vary from person to person. I've tried to include as many foods as possible in this four day rotation diet to allow for people's likes and dislikes, allergies and other practical considerations, such as seasonal availability, expense etc. There are other things to bear in mind as well. If you already have a history of allergy problems and eat only a limited number of foods, you may find yourself eating the same foods so regularly that you develop even more allergy problems and your diet becomes even more restricted. This is particularly true if you're a vegetarian, and even more so if you are a vegan. By varying your diet as much as possible, you are obtaining a wider spectrum of nutrients, boosting your immune system and minimising the risk of developing new allergies. At the same time allowing the body to lose some of its sensitivity to the foods which currently upset you. Some allergies may never be lost - fixed allergies (eg nuts) some people have a few of these and they tend to be the foods which upset you the most severely, and you may have to avoid these completely. Many people have a serious problem with wheat and other cereals. If this applies to you, then you may find it best to avoid all the grains in the grass family, (and possibly raw cane sugar, which is another member), to allow your immune system to lose some of its sensitivity. Don't be too disheartened if you feel worse for the first few days of this diet. If you get headache or just general aches and pains and feel 'out of sorts' You are probably hooked on a few foods and suffering withdrawal symptoms and it may be at least a week before you begin to feel the benefits.

All the fruits and vegetables, herbs and spices, for each day are grouped into food families. Buckwheat for instance, belongs to the same food family as rhubarb. There is now a delicious buckwheat pasta which you may find useful, but check the label to be sure all the ingredients suit you.

Soya beans belong to the legume family, so do peanuts, and if you react to one member of a food family, you may possibly get a cross reaction to other members and have to avoid those as well. Don't be afraid to adapt my recipes to suit your own individual needs. Many recipes contain nuts for instance, but for the most part, they are optional extras, and should be left out if you react to them. If possible only eat each member of a particular food family once every four days. Different members of the same food family, such as apples and pears, should strictly speaking be eaten on the same day. One of the exceptions I have made to this has been the grass family. All the members containing gluten are on day one and the others, millet, maize, rice and wild rice are on day three. This is because otherwise you would be left with a day with no complex carbohydrates to fill you up and give you enough calories for the day. If you react to foods from a particular family such as potatoes, then you may have to fill up on vegetables from another alternate day. As I said at the beginning of the book, you may find it easier to have a separate cupboard, or shelf, with perhaps colour coded stickers, of staple foods for each day so that it is less confusing. A four tier vegetable rack, also colour coded for each day, will be useful as well. This diet may seem daunting at first, but with a little patience and organisation the results are well worth the effort involved in setting it up.

If you have trouble finding some of the more obscure fruits and vegetables, such as yams, breadfruit, plantains and sweet potatoes, a trip to your nearest inner-city market with a large Asian and West Indian population should pay dividends. The stallholders I've met have been really helpful in offering hints and tips on how to cook unusual foods.

I've included hen's, duck's and quail's eggs for added variety, but please make sure that the hen's eggs are free range. As I said earlier additives are often included to battery hens' diets to improve the colour of the yolk. Some people react to all types of eggs so be very careful.

I recently invested in a juice extractor, which is very useful. Many of the fruits and vegetables of the day, on the rotation diet can be juiced and well diluted with double or more of the amount, of either sparkling mineral water or filtered tapwater. The leftover pulp can either be used up in soups and stews or puddings and cakes, as the case may be. However, I should point out that juices should be regarded as an occasional treat rather than a regular part of your daily diet. This is because without the fibre (which is left behind in the pulp) the juices are absorbed far too quickly into your bloodstream thereby making it more likely that you will become sensitised, whereas the whole fruit releases its sugars much more slowly. The vitamins and minerals in raw fruits and vegetables are vital to our good health and give a wonderful boost to our immune systems, especially in the winter months. Freshly juiced fruits and vegetables need to be consumed as soon after juicing as possible, as they quickly discolour, due to the enzymes coming into contact with oxygen.

The fruit and vegetable juices that we buy in supermarkets are usually heat treated to preserve them but unfortunately, this has the effect of destroying the enzymes that we need to help our body's metabolism to function properly. Enzymes are protein molecules which are able to cause specific chemical reactions to take place and are manufactured by every living organism for this purpose. Only very small amounts of each enzyme are needed to catalyse chemical reactions in living cells. Some enzymes can cause sugars to turn into fats, proteins etc. Living organisms contain many different kinds of enzymes, each with their own particular function. Enzymes perform a very important function in the stomach and intestines during digestion, helping digestive juices to break down the food we eat into its most digestible form so we are able to gain the maximum amount of nourishment from it. So in effect, the more raw fruits and vegetables we eat the better. Unfortunately, these enzymes are destroyed in foods that have been irradiated in order to extend their shelf lives. One of my biggest fears of genetically modified food is that the enzymes may be modified as well in order to extend the shelf life, and that the way we metabolise these hybrids may cause long term health damage, particularly for allergy sufferers who have enough problems already.

Wherever possible, buy organic fruit and vegetables, or if you have a plot of land big enough and the inclination, grow your own.

Some of the vegetables on day 3 of the rotation diet are hard to come by in supermarkets but are quite easy to grow in the average sized suburban garden and will give you several months worth of vegetables for very little outlay and effort. **Orach, (Mountain Spinach)** was widely cultivated in this country in Tudor times, until the introduction of true spinach, when its popularity died out. Nevertheless, the young tender leaves make an excellent addition to salads and the older tougher leaves can be cooked like spinach. There are red, green and white varieties and they are quite ornamental to look at. The plants grow from 3 to 5 ft high and seed should be sown out of doors in April. The seeds are quite hard and may need a good soaking if the weather is dry. The plants need good soil in order to thrive and may need thinning out once established to about 1½ feet apart. They may need earthing up and staking as they get bigger and the leaves can be pulled off on a 'cut and come again' basis.

Swiss Chard is not generally grown as a commercial crop because it is very bulky and wilts about 24 hours after being pulled. However, it has a very useful place in the allergy sufferer's garden, because it is so versatile and convenient, once established. The smallest and most tender leaves can be used in salads, and the large green leaves can be cooked like spinach. They actually taste better and boil down less than spinach does and the thick white stems can be cooked in bundles like asparagus. The plants are biennial and will produce flower stems in the second year and these can be cooked and eaten like sprouting broccoli. Swiss Chard is harvested by plucking off a few stems from the base of each plant and like Orach, this is done on a 'cut and come again' basis without stripping the plants completely of their leaves as this would kill them.

This crop is suited to any well drained soil that has been fed with organic manure. Sow from mid-March to the end of April and again in August, in drills 1½ inches deep and 18 inches apart thinning out the plants as they become established. Water often during the growing season and feed with liquid organic manure occasionally. The first crop should begin to yield in late summer and continue until late October. The plants are quite hardy and will survive the winter to produce another crop in spring before going to seed in early June. The second sowing (August) should be ready for use during the following May or June.

Good King Henry is a hardy perennial which is very easy to grow. Sow the seeds either in seed trays in the greenhouse or kitchen windowsill, or out of doors in early spring and thin out to 12 inches apart once the plants are established. In well nourished soil it produces good growth which is usually trouble free. It looks like kale in appearance but it tastes very much like asparagus when cooked and is well worth the effort of growing it.

Salsify is a little like a parsnip in appearance but the flavour is similar to that of oysters and goes well with a creamy sauce.

Sow out of doors in April or early May about 9" apart about an inch below the surface. Alternatively, you can start the seedlings off in a greenhouse, or a propagator on the kitchen windowsill. Then gently transplant them when they are about 2" high. The crop should be ready from early October onwards and lifted before the ground gets waterlogged.

Scorzonera. It is very much like a parsnip in flavour but its skin is almost black and the roots tend to be longer and thinner than parsnips. It can be peeled and roasted with meat, steamed or boiled until just tender. It can be grown and harvested in the same way as salsify.

Like all vegetables, they taste better from your own garden.

If you don't have a big enough garden, or you're a flat-dweller, then obviously this is not a practical prospect. However, there are some things that you can easily grow on a window sill that are both cheap and highly nutritious. Sprouted seeds such as Mung beans, Alfalfa sprouts, sprouted Chick peas, Lentils and Cress are all relatively quick and easy to grow. Many health food shops now stock custom made propagators and a wide range of pulses and seeds to sprout. Some are stacked so that you can grow several varieties at once without taking up too much space on your window ledge. Children are fascinated to see them growing and are often eager to help start them off. If you follow the instructions supplied with your propagator correctly, your first crop should be ready in about five to seven days.

Use them in your choice of the recipes on the Rotation Diet.

With all fruits and vegetables it is obviously important to retain as much nutritional content as possible.

Don't overcook vegetables - steam them whenever possible, or even better eat them raw. Buy them as fresh as possible and keep the water they were cooked in to use in soups or stews.

Store fruit and vegetables out of direct sunlight, for while this aids ripening of fruits and vegetables, it also hastens decay and destroys vitamin C.

Encourage young children to eat as many raw fruits and vegetables as they like. Make crudites with savoury dips such as houmous or guacamole. Many young children shun cooked vegetables but are happy to eat them raw.

CHAPTER THREE

COMPONENTS FOR A HEALTHY DIET

As you probably know already a well balanced diet consists of proteins, for growth and repair, complex carbohydrates which release their energy at a slow and steady rate to keep blood sugar levels regulated, vitamins and minerals for health and vitality and oils supplying essential fatty acids.

It is difficult to get a balanced, interesting and satisfying diet when you have to restrict your diet to the foods you tolerate.

We can encourage recovery by rotating the foods on a 4 day cycle and we always have something different to look forward to tomorrow.

By eating a balanced diet we build up our fragile health. This diet includes carbohydrates, fibre, protein, vitamins, minerals and sources of important fatty acids.

Complex carbohydrates give us slow release energy to keep us going until the next meal-time and are in foods such as potatoes, sweet potatoes and wild rice. Refined sugars on the other hand are simple carbohydrates which give us a quick fix of energy but don't satisfy our appetites and they can leave us craving more. The simple carbohydrates are bad news for those of us who have Candida fungal problems.

Fibre is provided by the variety of vegetables, fruits and grains available. There is a choice of protein to suit meat eaters and vegetarians.

The rotation diet has a choice of fresh fruits, vegetables, meat, cheese, eggs, fish and milk, to provide us with a balanced intake of vitamins and mineral traces. Refer to pages 147-152 for further information about vitamins and minerals. Those of you who are vegans must take doctors' or dieticians' advice about vitamin B12. Vitamin B12 is in meat, cheese and eggs but not in vegetables. Vitamin B12 deficiency is an extremely serious, indeed life threatening, condition.

Trace quantities of minerals are also needed to keep us healthy. For instance the potassium in fruit helps to regulate blood pressure.

Some readers may benefit from vitamin and mineral supplements. Supplements should be taken as directed by a doctor, to suit the needs of an individual. Inappropriate intake of supplements can have a negative effect on health, for instance, an excess of Vitamin C will only cause diarrhoea, but an excess of Vitamin A can be harmful.

The rotation diet also provides good sources of Essential Fatty Acids 'EFA's. EFAs are components of oils which the body cannot make but are needed to keep us healthy. Deficiencies can contribute to distressing conditions such as:

Impotence, Infertility, Stress, Sight or Hearing Problems, Poor Circulation, Dry Scaly Skin and inflammation such as that associated with Rheumatic Disease.

It is very difficult to get simple understandable, undistorted information about oils. Cooking oil refiners and margarine manufacturers, ably assisted by the advertising profession, extol the virtues of spreads and oils derived from Polyunsaturated Oils. However, manufacturing processes may damage polyunsaturated oils with the production of distorted fatty acids, called transfatty acids which are harmful and increase the risk of heart disease.

There are two types of essential fatty acids, omega 3's which are found in fresh wild fish, and flax seed oil and omega 6's found in evening primrose oil, borage oil (star flower oil) nuts and seeds. Fish from the following list are good sources:
Salmon, Trout, Mackerel, Sardines, Eel and to a lesser extent Tuna. Nuts such as Walnuts, Brazil Nuts and Almonds are good sources. Seeds such as Pumpkin, Sunflower, Flax (Linseed) and Hemp Seeds*, can be included in the diet and are also good sources. (* these are readily available in many health food shops and do not contain any narcotic substances in their seed form and so are not illegal to buy just don't try growing them!)

Some Cooking Oils such as Sunflower and Safflower <u>should</u> be good sources of EFAs. Most brands are processed to give high yields of oil but in doing so their chemical nature can be altered and undesirable impurities produced.

Extra Virgin Oils are the first fraction from the seed pressing and are generally better than the subsequent pressings. They should be stored in tightly lidded glass bottles, away from sunlight and should be used quickly. Plastic bottles should be avoided as trace chemical impurities can dissolve in the oil and upset sensitive people. Mono-unsaturated EFAs are believed to have a very protective function for our health and the best source is extra virgin olive oil.

Another natural oil which can be used in moderation for cooking is clarified butter, some people who are allergic to ordinary butter can tolerate clarified butter which has had its casein and albumen (milk protein) removed.

Dice around 8 oz (200 grams) butter into a heavy saucepan (preferably stainless steel or glass). Allow to melt over gentle heat and keep it cooking until it is foaming. Skim it well and strain through a muslin cheese cloth into a basin. Allow it to stand for a while until a layer of sediment forms in the bottom and decant the pure clarified butter into a suitable container leaving the sediment behind. Store in the fridge until needed.

Some readers may wish to take supplements which contain EFAs in concentrated early available forms. Evening Primrose Oil is a very well known example. Beware the outer capsule though. The gelatine shell can be derived from animal bi-products. Sensitive people may wish to squeeze the oil onto a spoon, before ingestion. There are other supplements and Star Flower Oil (from the Borage Plant) and Linseed and Marine Oils are examples. Nb Cod Liver Oil is not a good source of EFAs but is a rich source of Vitamin D, and also Vitamin A, which is harmful in excess, so the recommended dose must not be exceeded.

Despite some of the claims made on television, margarine type spreads are not without danger. Most contain traces of dairy products and saturated fats. There are some types, available from health food shops, which are combinations of oil and water, called emulsions, these often contain emulsifiers such as lecithin to keep them stable. If tolerated, they can be taken in moderation.

When hydogenation is used to produce margarine it gives rise to trans fatty acids; in this process a deodorised and purified oil is turned into a fat by pumping hydogen though it in the presence of a catalyst which is usually a compound of nickel or platinum. The oil is poured into a huge vat and hydrogen is bubbled through it along with the catalyst and rapid hardening takes place. It is at this molecular restructuring stage that trans-fats are created. Colourings such as annato or beta carotene may be added to improve the appearance and vitamins and flavourings are often added to make them more appealing to the consumers.

Some manufacturers are now aware of the dangers of trans fatty acids and are altering their manufacturing methods.

CHAPTER FOUR

THE ROTATION DIET

The rotation diet may seem complicated, with lots of things to think about but food is for enjoyment. Enjoy the diet, your body will tell you what is right for you. Don't allow yourself to be put off by well meaning friends or associates who, with the best will in the world, have no idea of the devastating effect that your allergies are having on your health. Once they see how much better you are they should be much more understanding. Above all else, don't let anyone make you feel isolated, deprived and sorry for yourself. After all how many people do you know who have to a large extent taken control of their own health?

LIST OF FOODS DAY 1

Meat
Beef, Tripe, Beef Dripping.
Ox Liver, Kidney, Stock, Tongue etc.

Fish
Tuna in Brine or Fresh Steaks.
Prawns and Shrimps
Halibut.
Skate.
Mullet, (Red or Grey).
Herring and Roes.
Monkfish.

Poultry
Ostrich Steaks.
Guinea Fowl and Eggs.

Dairy Products
Cow's Milk and Cream, Cheese, Butter and Live Yoghurt,
Fromage Frais and Cottage Cheese.

Vegetables
Pumpkin & Seeds. Marrow. Butter Nut Squash. Avocado and Oil. Cauliflower, Cabbage Chinese Leaves. Radish, Turnip, Watercress, Broccoli, Kale, Calabrese, Kohlrabi, Brussel Sprouts, Onion, Shallots and Chives, Garlic, Leeks & Asparagus, Courgettes, Gherkins. Cucumber Bamboo Shoots and Water Chestnuts.

Flour
Barley/Flour, Wholemeal Wheat Flour, Rye Flour, Ryvitas, Oats & Oakcakes. Oat Milk.

Fruits
Guava, Strawberries, Apples & Juice, Pears & Juice, Quince, Medlar, Rosehips, Plums and Prunes, Peach, Apricot, Nectarine, Damson, Blackberry, Cherry, Boysenberry, Melon, Water Melon.

Nuts & Oils
Macadamia Nuts. Chestnuts and Flour.
Almonds and Oil. Rapeseed Oil. Avocado Oil.

Beverages
Cocoa, Filtered Water, Diluted Fruit or Vegetable Juices.

Herbs & Spices
Pepper-Black and White. Cinnamon, Cloves, Bayleaf, Horse Radish, Mustard.

Miscellaneous
Malt or Cider Vinegar. Raw Cane Sugar.

LIST OF FOODS DAY 2

Meat
Pork and Dripping. Bacon, Ham, Black Pudding, Pig's Liver, Kidneys, Stock, etc.
Wild Boar with Offal as above.
Venison, Stock etc.

Fish
Salmon
Mussels, Oysters and Clams.
Cod, Stock and Roes.
Pollack and Hake
Octopus.

Poultry
Pheasant, Quail and Eggs.

Vegetables
Parsnips, Celery & Seeds, Carrots, Fennel & Seeds, Celeriac, Anise. Peas, Lentils - Cooked or Sprouted, and Flour. Also Lentil Flour or other Legume Pasta, Chick Peas, Cooked, Sprouted and Gram Flour, Mung Beans, Sprouted. Green Beans, Blackeyed Beans, Lima Beans, Kidney Beans, Butter Beans, Haricot Beans & Alfafa Sprouts. Cassava.

Soya Products
Soya Beans, Quorn, Tofu, Soya Yoghurt, Soya Margarine, Carob.

Flours
Arrowroot Flour, Tapioca & Flour Soya Flour, Carob Flour

Oils & Nuts
Olives and Oil, Peanuts & Oil, Grapeseed Oil. Pistachio Nuts, Cashews, Sesame Seeds and Oil, Tahini.

Fruits
Grapes, Sultanas and Raisins (unsulphured)
Pineapple and Juice.
Maple Syrup. Passion Fruit. Mango.
Halva with Grape Juice & Sultanas.

Beverages
Mate Tea, Indian or China Tea. Juices.

Herbs & Spices
Nutmeg, Mace, Angelica, (unsulphured),
Caraway, Coriander, Cumin, Parsley, Dill, Fenugreek, Lovage & Chervil, Samphire & Sweet Cicely, Liquorice & Senna.

Miscellaneous
Gelozone, Agar or Vegegel Gelling Agents.

LIST OF FOODS FOR DAY 3

Meat

Lamb and Dripping, Liver, Kidney, Stock etc.
Goat (available from specialist butchers, use as Lamb)

Fish

Mackerel
Plaice and Sole
Sardines and Pilchards (in brine)
Dab or Flounder Crab or Lobster.
Whitebait

Poultry

Free Range Chicken, Stock and Eggs
Partridge

Dairy Products

Sheep or Goat's Milk, Cheese & Live Homemade Yoghurt.

Vegetables

Mushrooms, Spinach, Beetroot, Swiss Chard, Good King Henry, Orache, Sweetcorn & Corn on the Cob, Chicory, Lettuce, Artichokes - Jerusalem & Globe, Salsify, Scorzonera, Endive, Yams, Bread Fruit, Okra, Chou-Chou, Turia Ginga.

Flours, Grains & By Products

Maize - Cornflakes - Maize Meal - Maize Pasta. Rice - Rice Krispies - Rice Cakes - Rice Milk, Wild Rice, Millet. Millet Milk.

Fruits

Figs, Pomegranates, Hops, Mulberries, Lychees.

Nuts, Seeds & Oils

Sunflower Oil & Seeds. Sunflower Oil. Walnuts and oil, Pecans, Butternuts, Hickory Nuts.

Herbs & Spices
Allspice (Jamaican Pepper)
Spearmint, Peppermint, Applemint, Thyme, Winter Savoury, Summer Savoury, Basil, Sage, Pineapple Sage, Lemon Balm, Oregano, Marjoram, Tarragon, Bergamot,
Comfrey Hyssop, Rosemary & Lavender.

Beverages
Camomile Tea, Coffee (Ground decaffeinated) Comfrey Tea. Peppermint Tea. Prewitt's Chicory, Dandelion Coffee.

Sweeteners
Beet Sugar, Honey.

LIST OF FOODS FOR DAY 4

Meat

Rabbit Hare and Stock

Poultry

Turkey and Stock.
Goose and Stock.
Duck Stock and Eggs.
Grouse
Woodpigeon.

Fish

Shark Steaks/Swordfish Steaks, Haddock, Squid. Trout,
Cockles, Scallops, Seabass, Sea Bream, Tilapia,
Red Snapper/Pink Snapper.
Gurnet/Grouper.
Eel Steaks.

Vegetables

Potatoes and Flour.
Peppers, Red Green and Yellow.
Tamarillo, (Tree Tomatoes)
Tomatoes & Aubergines, Chilli Peppers & Pimentos. Plantains,
Green Bananas.

Flour and Grains

Buckwheat, Grains, Pasta and Flour. Sago, and Flour. Banana Flour

Nuts, Oils & Fats

Coconut & Coconut Milk. Tomor, Margarine,
Palm Oil. Hazelnuts and Oil, Filberts, Cobnuts, Brazil Nuts.

Fruits

Dates & Date Sugar.
Sharron Fruit/Persimmons, Kiwi Fruit, Gooseberries,
Rhubarb, Banana Pawpaw & Papaya, Currants, Red or Blackcurrants
and Juice. Cranberries and Juice. Oranges, Lemons, Limes,
Grapefruit, Tangerines, Satsumas, Mandarins, Citron & Kumquats.

Herbs & Spices
Cayenne Pepper, Paprika Pepper, Ginger, Turmeric, Cardamon, Sorrel, Lemon, Verbena, Vanilla Pods.

Beverages
Diluted Fruit or Vegetable Juices,
Lemon & Ginger Tea, Mineral Water.

Sweetener
Fructose.

LIST OF DRINKS FOR DAY ONE

Cocoa/Drinking Chocolate, (with raw Cane Sugar)
Cow's Milk
Apple juice
(cold pressed or freshly juiced if possible)
Very well diluted with either
Filtered or Mineral Water
Freshly Juiced Strawberries well diluted with Sparkling Mineral Water

LIST OF BREAKFASTS FOR DAY ONE

Wholewheat Toast
Oat Cakes with Butter and choice of Strawberry, Blackberry or other Jam from day's list.
Porridge with Filtered Water or Cow's Milk & Cream
Wholemeal, Rye or Barley Flour Pancakes with Guinea Fowl Eggs.
Cream and Fruits of the day.
Savoury Wholemeal, Rye or Barley Flour Pancakes,
With Fromage Frais, Spring Onions and Chives
Live Yoghurt with Fruits of the day.
Your choice of fruits of the day alone
Poached, Boiled or Fried Guinea Fowl Eggs
Herb Omelette of Guinea Fowl Eggs.

LIST OF SOUPS/STARTERS FOR DAY ONE

Asparagus Soup
Kidney Soup
French Onion Soup
Tuna Salad with Avocado and Prawns
Avocado Dip with Crudites (Vegetarian)

LIST OF LUNCHES/MAIN MEALS FOR DAY ONE

Monk Fish Kebabs
Prawn Stir Fry with strips of Monk Fish (Optional) With Vegetarian Alternative.
Beef Stuffed Marrow.
Vegetarian Stuffed Marrow.
Butter Nut Squash with Sweet Potatoes and Courgettes, (Vegetarian)
Spaghetti Bolognaise
Braised Steak with Wholemeal, Rye or Barley Flour Dumplings.
Grilled Halibut or Turbot Steaks
Grilled Herrings.
Liver and Onion Casserole.
Stuffed Rump Steak.
Beefburgers with Horseradish.
Wholemeal, Rye or Barley Flour Pancakes (Vegetarian)
Skate Wings in a Herb and Butter Sauce
Grilled Red or Grey Mullet
Guinea Fowl Omelette (Vegetarian)
Roast Guinea Fowl
Wholemeal, Rye or Barley Flour Quiche with Guinea Fowl Eggs (Vegetarian)
Halibut Pie with Cheese Topping
Stir Fried Herring Roes
Cheese and Onion Pasties with Wholemeal, Rye or Barley Flour Pastry (Vegetarian)
Corned Beef and Onion Pasties
Pan fried, Grilled or Barbecued Ostrich Steaks
Steak and Kidney Pie.

LIST OF DESSERTS FOR DAY ONE

Apple Crumble
Apple and Blackberry or Plum Crumble
Guava and Strawberry Fruit Salad
Apple Pie
Apple and Blackberry Pie
Plum Pie
Creme Broulee

SNACKS/OCCASIONAL TREATS

Fresh Fruits and Nuts of the Day.
Homemade Sticky Bonfire Toffee, With Cream, Butter and Raw Cane Sugar.
Wholemeal Bread
Apple and Cinnamon Muffins
Apple and Blackberry Muffins
Jam Tarts
Soda Bread
Chocolate Caramel Shortcake Bars
Oat Cakes & Butter & Jam Made with Cane Sugar
And Fruits of the Day
Oil Chocolate Cake
Flapjacks
Strawberry Dairy Ice Cream.

BREAKFASTS FOR DAY ONE

Refer to (Day One) Menu List for all other Breakfast items

Choice of Fruits of the Day (With or without Live Cow's Milk Yoghurt)

This can be bought Live yoghurt or you can make your own.

LIVE YOGHURT

Simply boil up enough Cow's Milk to fill a wide necked Thermos Flask. Allow to cool to blood heat. Pour into the flask but don't quite fill it. Add one teaspoonful of yoghurt culture, such as Vital Dophilus, screw the top down tight and leave for twenty four hours. The yoghurt is then ready. For making further batches of yoghurt, retain about half a cupful and use as a starter. The first two or three batches may be a bit on the watery side but then the batches should start to get much creamier. If the culture starts to produce thinner yoghurt after several preparations add another teaspoonful of Vital Dophilus, or other culture. You can use the same method to produce Sheep's or Goat's or Soya Milk Yoghurt to use on rotation. The cultures used in the production of live yoghurt are in the family of friendly bacteria that normally live in the digestive tract and aid digestion as well as enhancing our immune systems. Please don't take this to mean that you should have live yoghurt every day of one sort or another, you need as much variety in your diet as possible to obtain as wide a spectrum of nutrients as possible.

WHOLEMEAL, RYE OR BARLEY FLOUR PANCAKES

* 6 oz (125 grams) Wholemeal, Rye or Barley Flour
* 2 Guinea Fowl Eggs or a raised dessertspoonful of Cornflour (from day 3)
* Pinch of Sea Salt.
* Filtered Water or Cow's Milk and Water.

Place flour and salt in a mixing bowl. Make a well in the centre and add the two eggs. (It may be wise to crack them one at a time into a separate bowl first to check for freshness). If you prefer you can use cornflour to bind the mixture together. Slake it down with enough filtered water to make a smooth lumpfree paste, add more water to make it runny then add to flour and mix to required consistency. Fry the pancakes in the usual way, with either rapeseed oil or butter. Serve either with fruits of the day, or try a savoury version with Fromage Frais, spring onions and chives.

HERB OMELETTE WITH GUINEA FOWL EGGS (DAY ONE)

* 4 Guinea Fowl Eggs per person
* Pinch of Sea Salt and freshly ground Black Pepper
* Choice of freshly chopped Herbs of the day (to taste)
* Butter or Rapeseed Oil.

Beat the eggs, seasoning and herbs together and make the omelettes in the usual way. Also try guinea fowl eggs poached, fried, boiled or scrambled.

SOUPS/STARTERS FOR DAY ONE
ASPARAGUS SOUP (VEGETARIAN)

* Vegetable Stock of The Day (enough to cover and fill up the pan)
* Mixed vegetables from day's list (eg. Cabbage, Broccoli, Turnips, Cauliflower & Kale)
* 2 or 3 Leeks (sliced thinly)
* 1 or 2 Cloves of Garlic (crushed and to taste)
* 1 Bundle of Fresh Asparagus (or 15oz can)
* Rapeseed Oil or Butter
* 2 Bayleaves
* 2 or 3 Tablespoons Live Cow's Milk Yoghurt.

Sweat the bayleaves, leeks and garlic in a heavy bottomed saucepan with the oil or butter for about five minutes. Add the vegetable stock and bring to the boil. Drop in the bundle of asparagus and other vegetables and lower the heat. Simmer until the asparagus is tender. Allow to cool before blending in a liquidiser. Reheat and serve adding a swirl of fresh cream and a little freshly chopped watercress if liked. 4-6 people.

KIDNEY SOUP

* 8oz (200 grams) Ox Kidneys
* 2 pints/just under 1 litre of Beef Stock, (not Stock Cubes unless you check label first).
* Bouquet Garni
* 1oz Butter or Rapeseed Oil
* 1 large Onion finely chopped
* 1 rounded tablespoon Wholemeal, Rye or Barley Flour
* 1 Bayleaf
* Sea Salt and freshly ground Black Pepper to taste.

Skin and core the kidneys. Soak in cold salted water for an hour. Drain, slice and put into a pan with the bouquet garni, bayleaf and half the beef stock. Cover and simmer until the stock is reduced and the kidneys are tender. Meanwhile melt the butter or heat oil in a pan. Add the chopped onion and fry gently until brown. Stir in the flour and remaining beef stock, season and stir until boiling, add to the pan with the kidneys and simmer for ten minutes. Allow to cool then either rub through a sieve or mix in an electric blender. Reheat and thicken if necessary with a little arrowroot mixed to a paste with filtered water.
4-6 people.

FRENCH ONION SOUP (DAY ONE)

* 1lb (400 grams) Onions
* 2oz (50 grams) Butter or Rapeseed Oil
* 1 rounded tablespoonful Wholemeal, Rye or Barley Flour
* 2 pints (just under 1 litre) of beef stock or filtered water
* 2 Bayleaves
* Sea Salt and freshly ground Black Pepper

Heat the margarine in a heavy bottomed saucepan. Add finely chopped onions, lower the heat and cook gently until golden brown, stirring occasionally. Stir in the flour and cook for two or three minutes more. Meanwhile heat stock or water to boiling point in another pan and add to the onions and flour. Add the bayleaf and seasoning and simmer gently for around thirty minutes. Serve with

thick chunks of wholemeal bread and a generous sprinkling of cheese if liked and tolerated or perhaps barley flour soda bread.
4-6 people.

TUNA SALAD WITH AVOCADO AND PRAWNS (DAY ONE)

* 1 Fresh Tuna Steak Per Person (grilled or panfriend and allowed to cool, then boned and flaked into chunks)
* 8oz (200 grams) prepared and cooked Prawns.
* 2/3 Ripe Avocados, (peeled, halved and sliced)
* 1 Small Head of Chinese Leaves (chopped finely)
* 2 Bunches Radishes
* 1 Bunch of chopped Spring Onions
* Chopped Chives
* 2 Raw Courgettes either sliced or cut in Julienne Strips
* 1 Pak-Choi (peeled and chopped - optional)
* 1/4 Raw White Cabbage (shredded)
* 1 Tin Bamboo Shoots (optional)
* 1 Tin Water Chestnuts (optional)

The method is pretty obvious, just mix all the prepared ingredients together in a large serving bowl, toss together and serve. But note that if using bamboo shoots and water chestnuts that they should be well rinsed in filtered water before adding to the rest of the ingredients. For a more substantial meal you could serve with jacket sweet potatoes and a dressing of almond or avocado oil, mustard, fresh horseradish root, with a little cream and cider vinegar. With a sprinkling of pumpkin seeds.
4-6 people.

Pak-Choi look rather like smooth parsnips. They can be peeled and eaten raw in salads, stir fried or boiled in filtered salted water. They are available in some supermarkets now and many large city markets where you can buy all kinds of unusual fruits and vegetables such as yams, okra, casava and sweet potatoes.
Note: You could substitute ox tongue for the tuna if you prefer, or cold sliced roast beef.

AVOCADO DIP WITH CRUDITES (VEGETARIAN)
DAY ONE STARTER

* 2 Ripe Avocados
* 1 Small Onion finely chopped
* Handful finely chopped Chives
* Handful finely chopped fresh Watercress
* Handful Pumpkin Seeds
* Mustard (to taste)
* Live Yoghurt (to taste)
* Fromage Frais (to taste)

Whiz all the prepared ingredients together in a blender with enough live yoghurt and fromage frais to get the required consistency. Sprinkle with slivered almonds and macadamia nuts if tolerated and serve with crudites of courgette sticks, cauliflower florets, spring onions and radishes. Serves up to 4 people.

LUNCHES/MAIN MEALS FOR DAY ONE

BARBECUED MONKFISH KEBABS
(Portuguese Recipe)

* 1lb (400 grams) Cubed Monkfish
* ½ lb (200 grams) King Prawns (peeled)
* 2 Courgettes thickly sliced
* Several very small Onions or Shallots (peeled but left whole)

In Portugal the stalks of bayleaves are soaked in water and used instead of skewers for these tasty kebabs as they impart a flavour of their own to the finished dish, but like me, you will probably have to make do with metal skewers instead. Place alternative cubes of monkfish, prawns and all the other ingredients along the skewers. Brush with melted butter or rapeseed oil and place on a barbecue or under a medium hot grill turning frequently so as not to burn the outside before it is cooked through to the middle. Monkfish varies in its cooking time depending on the age of the fish so you will need to use your own judgement as to when it's cooked.

Serves 4 people with jacket sweet potatoes and a green salad of watercress, Chinese leaves, rocket leaves, spring onions, radishes and slices of Avocado.

PRAWN STIR FRY WITH STRIPS OF MONKFISH (OPTIONAL) (DAY ONE)

* 8oz (200 grams) prepared Prawns
* 8oz (200 grams) Monkfish cut into thin strips (optional)
* 1 Bunch Spring Onions (chopped finely)
* 2 Courgettes (sliced thinly or cut into Julienne strips)
* Chopped Chives
* 1 Tin Water Chestnuts
* 1 Tin Bamboo Shoots
* I Head of Chinese Leaves (shredded)
* Freshly chopped watercress and rocket leaves.
* 2oz (50 grams) Almonds or Macadamia Nuts (optional)
* Few sliced Radishes
* Sea Salt and freshly ground Black Pepper
* Rapeseed or Almond Oil for stir frying

Heat the oil in a heavy wok or large frying pan and stirfry all the ingredients until the prawns and monkfish are tender. Serves up to 4 people, with jacket sweet potatoes and Avocados, this mixture could be used as an alternative stuffing for marrow.

VEGETARIAN ALTERNATIVE

Omit the prawns and monkfish and add 4oz (100 grams) slivered almonds and 4oz (100 grams) sliced chestnuts instead, with a generous sprinkling of pumpkin seeds.

BEEF STUFFED MARROW (DAY ONE)

* 1½ lb (600 grams) minced lean steak
* 1 large Onion (finely chopped)
* 1 large Marrow
* Sea Salt and freshly ground Black Pepper to taste
* Rapeseed Oil or Clarifed Butter

Fry the minced beef and onion in the oil over low heat, until pale golden brown. Season to taste. Meanwhile slice the marrow in half length ways and scoop out the seeds from both halves. Fill the cavities with the minced beef and onion. Place the two halves together and fasten with twine before baking in a pre-heated moderate oven for approximately one hour and fifteen minutes in a covered dish. Serve with cabbage, cauliflower, baked sweet potatoes and courgettes.

VEGETARIAN STUFFED MARROW Note, for alternative fillings see previous recipe for which there is also a vegetarian option. Serves 4-6 people.

BUTTERNUT SQUASH WITH SWEET POTATOES AND COURGETTES DAY ONE (VEGETARIAN)

* 1 Good sized Butternut Squash
* 2-3 Sweet Potatoes
* 3 Courgettes
* 1lb (400 grams) Chestnuts (tinned will do if you can't get fresh)
* 8oz (200 grams) Whole Almonds
* Pumpkin Seeds (to taste)
* 4oz (100 grams) Macadamia Nuts
* Few Cloves (optional)
* Freshly Chopped Watercress and Rocket Leaves (to taste)
* Rapeseed or Almond Oil

Cut the butternut squash in half. Remove the seeds and the surrounding soft pulp and discard, (unless you want to save the seeds and try to grow your own). Don't bother to peel it, just cut it into generous sized chunks, it's much easier to get the skin off once it's cooked. Peel the sweet potatoes and cut into similar sized chunks to the squash. Place in a roasting dish with the cloves if using and drizzle the oil over it all, before putting into a moderate oven and baking for around thirty minutes. Add the sliced courgettes, chestnuts, almonds and macadamia nuts and bake for a further fifteen minutes, basting occasionally until the squash and sweet potatoes are golden brown. Serve with a sprinkling of pumpkin seeds, white cheese and garnish with the freshly chopped herbs. Serves 4-6 people with a green salad of watercress, Chinese leaves and rocket with Avocados, raw courgettes and an almond oil, cider vinegar and mustard dressing.

SPAGHETTI BOLOGNAISE (DAY ONE)

* 1lb (400 grams) Minced Beef
* 1 Medium sized Onion (finely chopped)
* 2 Bayleaves (cracked)
* Sea Salt and freshly ground Black Pepper (to taste)
* Rapeseed Oil or Melted Butter
* Beef and Vegetable Stock or Filtered Water
* 1 Large can of Chopped Plum Tomatoes (borrowed from day four so don't eat them again until next true rotation)

Brown the minced beef and onion in a heavy bottomed saucepan with the oil. Add the tomatoes, bayleaves and either filtered water or beef and vegetable stock to cover. Bring to the boil, season and simmer for around forty five minutes. Meanwhile, prepare the wholewheat spaghetti following the instructions on the packet. Serve with choice of vegetables from the day's list. Serves 4-6 people.

BRAISED STEAK WITH WHOLEMEAL, RYE OR BARLEY FLOUR DUMPLINGS (DAY ONE)

* 1lb (400 grams) Braising Steak
* 1 Medium Onion (finely chopped)
* 2 Bayleaves
* Sea Salt and freshly ground Black Pepper
* Rapeseed Oil
* Filtered Water or Beef and Vegetable Stock
* Salt and pepper

For the Dumplings

* 8oz (200 grams) Wholemeal, Rye or Barley Flour
* 4oz (100 grams) either Beef or Vegetable Suet
* 1 Rounded teaspoonful Cream of Tartar
* 1 Level teaspoonful Bicarbonate of Soda
* Filtered Water

Brown the steak to seal in the juices and put in a casserole dish with the chopped onion and bayleaves. Pour over the stock or filtered water, season to taste, cover and cook in a moderate oven for one and a half hours before you make the dumplings in the usual way, add them to the beef and cook for a further thirty minutes. Serve with choice of vegetables of the day and jacket sweet potatoes, if liked. Save and freeze any leftover meat juices and vegetable water to make stock for soup on the rotation diet.
Serves 4-6 people.

GRILLED HALIBUT OR TURBOT STEAKS (DAY ONE)

* 1 Good sized Fish Steak Per Person
* Sea Salt and freshly ground Black Pepper
* Rapeseed Oil or Melted Butter

These fish are firm fleshed and are some of the best for grilling as they hold their shape and are less likely to break up when being turned. Simply brush with oil and season with salt and pepper before placing under a medium hot grill. Cook until golden brown, turning once. Serve with a sprinkling of fresh watercress and your choice of vegetables of the day.

GRILLED HERRINGS (DAY ONE)

* 1 Cleaned Herring Per Person
* Sea Salt and freshly ground Black Pepper
* Rapeseed Oil or Melted Butter.

Make deep cuts along the sides of the fish, brush with oil and season well before placing under a medium grill, cook for around four or five minutes each side turning once. For split or filleted herring, brush with oil and grill on cut side first for around five minutes, then turn and allow two to three minutes on the skin side. Serve either hot with jacket sweet potatoes, cauliflower, cabbage and courgettes, or cold with a salad of Chinese leaves, radishes, spring onions, chives, avocado, rocket and shredded white cabbage. You could add slivers of almonds and a scattering of fresh watercress with a dressing of almond oil, mustard and cider vinegar.

LIVER AND ONION CASSEROLE (DAY ONE)

* 1lb (400 grams) Ox Liver (washed and sliced)
* 2 Onions (finely chopped)
* 1 Small Turnip
* 1 Bayleaf
* Beef and Vegetable Stock or Filtered Water

Coat the liver in seasoned wholemeal, rye or barley flour and brown in a frying pan to seal in the juices. Put alternate layers of liver, onions and turnip into an ovenproof dish. Cover with hot vegetable and beef stock or filtered water and season to taste. Cover and cook for an hour or so in a moderate oven, or until the liver is tender. Serves 4 with your choice of vegetables of the day.

STUFFED RUMP STEAK (DAY ONE)

- 1½ lbs (600 grams) Lean Rump Steak (one piece about 1½ inches thick with a pocket cut in it for the filling)
- Sea Salt and freshly ground Black Pepper
- Rapeseed Oil, Melted Butter or Almond Oil for brushing

For the filling:

- 1 Courgette (finely sliced)
- 3-4 finely chopped Spring Onions or a decent sized Shallot if these are not available
- Small amount of freshly grated Horseradish Root (optional)
- 2 Bayleaves.
- 1oz (25 grams) Chopped Almonds (optional)
- 4 Radishes (thinly sliced)
- 2 oz (50 grams) Roasted and Minced Chestnuts (optional)

Soften the onions or shallot and courgettes in oil. Add the bayleaves, nuts if using, and radishes. Draw off the heat, season well with salt and pepper. Allow to cool a little and take out the bayleaves before stuffing the mixture into the cavity in the rump steak. Fasten the pocket shut with either meat skewers or sew it shut with stout twine (not coloured twine, obviously as the colour may leach out during cooking). Brush with oil and place under a medium grill for five to eight minutes either side. Garnish with fresh watercress and serve with your choice of vegetables of the day.
Serves 4-6 people.

BEEFBURGERS WITH HORSERADISH (DAY ONE)

- 1lb (400 grams) Minced Beef
- 1 Onion (finely chopped)
- Little grated fresh Horseradish Root if available, otherwise use bought Horseradish Sauce (check label first) use to taste
- Sea Salt and freshly ground Black Pepper

Mix all the ingredients together in a large bowl. Divide into either eight small or four large burgers. Place on a barbecue or under a preheated grill and cook gently, turning frequently until brown. Serves 4 people with your choice of vegetables.

WHOLEMEAL, RYE OR BARLEY FLOUR PANCAKES (DAY ONE)

* 6oz Wholemeal, Rye or Barley Flour
* 2 Guinea Fowl Eggs
* Pinch of Sea Salt
* Filtered Water (or Cow's Milk and Water to bind)

Place dry ingredients in a mixing bowl. Make a well in the centre and add the two eggs. It may be as well to crack them one at a time into a separate bowl first to check for freshness. Blended to a smooth paste with milk or filtered water to bind and blend in more filtered water, or Cow's milk and water to get the required consistency. Make pancakes in the usual way. Serve either with stewed fruits of the day or try a savoury version with fromage frais, spring onions and chopped chives, garnished with watercress.
Makes 6-8 pancakes.

SKATE WINGS IN A HERB AND BUTTER SAUCE

* 4 Skate Wings
* 2oz (500 grams) Butter or Rapeseed Oil
* Fresh Watercress
* 1oz (25 gram) Wholemeal, Rye or Barley Flour
* 2 Bayleaves
* 3/4 pint Fish Stock (strained)
* 1 Bunch Spring Onions (finely chopped)
* Handful Chives (finely chopped)
* 4oz (100 grams) Double Cream
* 2oz Fromage Frais
* Sea Salt and freshly ground Black Pepper

Ask your fishmonger to skin the skate wings for you as they are not at all easy to do yourself. Heat the butter or oil in a large skillet pan. It needs to be big enough to take all the fish in a single layer. Put the fish in the pan when the butter starts to spit. Season with salt and pepper and reduce the heat. Cover and cook gently for two or three minutes each side. Meanwhile mix the flour to a smooth paste with a little of the fish stock in a saucepan. Gradually add the rest of the fish stock, along with the bayleaves, spring onions, chives and a little of the watercress (Reserve the rest for garnishing). Bring to the boil, stirring constantly. Reduce the heat and carry on stirring until the sauce thickens. Pour the sauce over the skate and carry on cooking it for about twenty minutes or until the fish is cooked through. Lift the fish out carefully onto a warm serving dish and keep warm. Add the fromage frais and double cream to the sauce stir well and season if necessary. Simmer gently for about five minutes. Take out the bayleaves and pour the sauce over the fish. Garnish with watercress, and chopped chives. Serves 4 people, with your choice of vegetables of the day.

GRILLED RED OR GREY MULLET (DAY ONE)

* 1 Red or Grey Mullet Per Person
* Sea Salt and freshly ground Black Pepper
* Rapeseed, avocado or Almond Oil

Scrape off the scales and remove the fins from the fish. Slice the belly open and remove the gut, but it is usual to leave the liver inside as it imparts its own distinctive flavour to the fish. Brush the fish with oil season with salt and pepper and place under a medium hot grill. Cook for about five minutes each side depending on the size of the fish. Serve with your choice of vegetables of the day and garnish with freshly chopped chives, watercress and pumpkin seeds if you wish.

GUINEA FOWL OMELETTE (DAY ONE) (VEGETARIAN)

* 4-6 Guinea Fowl Eggs Per Person
* Your choice of the following fillings: Spring Onions, Courgettes, Water Chestnuts, Chives, Watercress, Fromage Frais or Hard White Cheese.

Season with salt and pepper and make omelettes in the usual way.

ROAST GUINEA FOWL (DAY ONE)

* 1 Good sized Guinea Fowl
* Sea Salt and freshly ground Black Pepper
* Butter, or Rapeseed Oil for basting

Wash the bird inside and out in salted water. Pat dry with kitchen paper (not bleached or coloured paper). Place the bird in a roasting dish and either rub all over with softened butter or baste with oil. Season and roast in a moderate oven for fifteen minutes per pound and fifteen minutes over, or until crisp and golden brown. It's best to roast the bird upside down for the first half of the cooking time to allow the meat juices to run down into the breast to make it more succulent and moist, turn over and baste for the second half of cooking. Serves 4 people with vegetables and herbs of your choice from the day's list.

WHOLEMEAL, RYE OR BARLEY FLOUR QUICHE WITH GUINEA FOWL EGGS (DAY ONE) VEGETARIAN

For the shortcrust pastry:

* 8oz (200 grams) Wholemeal, Rye or Barley Flour
* 4oz (100 grams) Butter
* Filtered Water to bind

For the filling:

* 4 Guinea Fowl Eggs
* ½ pint (270 ml) Cow's Milk
* 6oz (150 grams) grated White Cheese
* 2 or 2 Spring Onions (sliced finely)
* 2 large Courgettes (sliced thinly)
* Handful chopped Chives
* Chopped Watercress
* Sea Salt and freshly ground Black Pepper.

Line two eight inch diameter flan tins with the pastry and bake blind for ten minutes in a moderate oven. Meanwhile, crack the guinea fowl eggs one at a time into a separate bowl to check that they are fresh. Add the cow's milk and season, beat well. Take the pastry cases out of the oven and divide the cheese, onions, courgettes and herbs between the two quiches. Pour the eggs and milk over the filling, scatter a little more cheese on top and return to the oven. Reduce the heat slightly and bake until golden brown and firm to the touch. Serves 4-6 people with your choice of vegetables and herbs of the day.

FISH PIE WITH CHEESE TOPPING (DAY ONE)

* 1½lb (600 grams) Halibut (steamed, skinned and boned)
* 6oz (150 grams) Fromage Frais
* Cow's Milk
* Handful Chopped Chives
* 1-2 Cloves of Garlic (to taste)
* 1lb Broccoli Florets (lightly steamed)
* Grated Hard White Cheese

Flake the fish into an ovenproof dish with the broccoli, mix the cream cheese with enough milk to get a thick creamy consistency. Add the herbs and crushed garlic and pour over the fish. Sprinkle generously with grated cheese and bake in a moderate oven until golden brown. Serve with choice of vegetables from the day's list.
4-6 people.

STIR FRIED HERRING ROES (DAY ONE)

* 1lb (400 grams) Herring Roes (sliced)
* ½lb (200 grams) Herring Fillets (cut into thin strips)
* 1 Medium Onion (chopped finely)
* 2 Large Courgettes (sliced thinly)
* 1 Tin Bamboo Shoots
* 1 Tin Water Chestnuts
* Chopped Chives (to taste)
* Handful Chopped Watercress
* 2oz (50 grams) Slivered Almonds (optional)
* Rapeseed Oil, Melted Butter or Almond Oil
* Live Yoghurt (optional)

Heat the oil in a wok and add the herring roes and strips of fish. Add the vegetables and stir constantly or keep shaking the wok so that the food is evenly cooked. This shouldn't take more than a couple of minutes. Add the herbs and nuts if you're using them, pour over the live yoghurt, seasom, warm the dish through and serve with your choice of vegetables of the day.
Serves 4-6 people.

CHEESE AND ONION PASTIES (VEGETARIAN) (DAY ONE)

* 8oz (200 grams) Wholemeal, Rye or Barley Flour
* 4oz (100 grams) Butter or Sunflower Marg from Day 3
* 1 Rounded teaspoonful Cream of Tartar
* 1 level teaspoonful Bicarbonate of Soda
* Grated White Cheese
* Finely Chopped Onion
* Choice of freshly chopped herbs of the day (optional)
* Filtered Water.

Make shortcrust pastry in the usual way with your choice of flour, butter or sunflower margarine and mixing agents, using just enough filtered water to bind to a stiff dough. (The less water used, the shorter the pastry). If you have enough time, chill the pastry for half an hour in the fridge before rolling out in the usual way. I use a saucer as a template to cut around, then wet one half of the circle, put filling in the middle and bring the edges up to meet in the centre. Pinch the edges together, nipping them between your fingers and thumbs to form a zig-zag pattern along the middle. Brush with milk and bake in a moderate oven until golden brown. Makes 4 pasties.
For a change, try corned beef and onion and perhaps add leftover vegetables and a few freshly chopped herbs for a packed lunch or picnic.

GRILLED, FRIED OR BARBECUED OSTRICH STEAKS (DAY ONE)

Take a good sized piece of ostrich fillet or rump (about a pound in weight) and cut across the grain to form medallions about half an inch thick. If grilling or barbecuing brush with either rapeseed, almond oil or butter and cook as you would do a medium rare beef steak, leaving the meat slightly pink in the centre. If you overcook ostrich meat it will become tough as there is virtually no fat present to help make it tender. To fry it, sear the meat quickly to seal in the juices and finish off on a low heat for a few minutes. Serve garnished with choice of herbs and a selection of vegetables of the day, and maybe jacket sweet potatoes.
Serves 4 people.
Further on in the book, past the rotation diet section, I have included a few more ostrich meat recipes reproduced by kind permission of OSGROW Ltd. Tybroughton Hall, Whitchurch, Shropshire SY13 3BB. Tel: 01948 780654 Fax: 01948 780664. I am sure they would be pleased to forward details of their regional suppliers who deliver the meat to your door and present you with a free recipe book.

STEAK AND KIDNEY PIE (DAY ONE)

* 1½lb (600 grams) Steak or Steak and Kidney
* Beef Stock
* 1 Medium Onion
* 2-3 Bayleaves
* Sea Salt and Fresh Black Pepper
* 8oz Wholemeal, Rye or Barley Flour
* 4oz Butter
* 1 Rounded teaspoonful Cream of Tartar
* 1 Level teaspoonful Bicarbonate of Soda
* Melted Butter or Rapeseed Oil for frying

Heat the oil in a heavy saucepan or skillet. Brown the meat to seal in the juices. Add the onion and soften before placing in a casserole dish with the meat, bayleaves and herbs. Season and cover with beef or vegetable stock. Cook in a moderate oven for one hour and forty five minutes until the meat is tender and the stock is reduced. Make up the pastry in the usual way with your choice of flour. Roll out a piece big enough to cover the top of the casserole dish. Brush the top with milk if tolerated, return to the oven and bake for another fifteen or twenty minutes until golden brown. Serves 4 people with your choice of vegetables of the day.

DESSERTS FOR DAY ONE

APPLE CRUMBLE

* 2lb (800 grams) Cooking Apples (peeled and sliced)
* Raw Cane Sugar, if tolerated or choice of either pure Rosehip Syrup or concentrated pure Apple Juice to sweeten to taste.
* 8oz (200 grams) Wholemeal, Rye, or Barley Flour
* 4oz of Butter
* 2oz (50 grams) Chopped Almonds or Macadamia Nuts (optional)

Stew the fruit with your choice of sweetener. Allow to cool before putting the apples into an ovenproof dish and covering with the crumble topping and nuts if used. Bake at 190c for fifteen to twenty minutes.

Variations: Substitute plums or prunes for the filling to include blackberries if in season. Or add a teaspoonful of cinnamon. Serves 4 people.

Cook's Tip

Drizzle enough filtered water into the crumbs to firm them and the crumble topping will have a much crunchier texture.

STRAWBERRY AND GUAVA FRUIT SALAD (DAY ONE)

* 2 Guavas (Sliced or cut into segments)
* 1lb (400 grams) fresh Strawberries
* 2 Dessert Apples (washed, cored and sliced)
* 2 Pears
* ½ Melon cubed or Melon Balls
* ½lb (200 grams) Blackberries
* ½lb (200 grams) Boysenberries
* 2 Peaches (peeled and sliced)
* 2 Apricots (peeled and sliced)
* 4 Plums (stoned and halved)
* Apple Juice

Simply put all the prepared ingredients into a big enough salad bowl, pour over enough apple juice to cover and serve with cream if liked and tolerated. This can either be served at breakfast or as an after dinner dessert.
Serves 4-6 people.

APPLE PIE (DAY ONE)

* 1lb (400 grams) Wholemeal, Spelt, Rye or Barley Flour
* 8oz Butter
* 3/4 teaspoonful Cream of Tartar
* 1/4 teaspoonful Bicarbonate of Soda
* 2lb (800 grams) Baking Apples
* Pinch of Cinnamon (optional)
* Ether Raw Cane Sugar, Pure Rosehip Syrup or Concentrated Apple Juice to sweeten to taste.

Peel and slice the apples. Put into a heavy bottomed saucepan with a little filtered water. Once the apples are stewed, sweeten them to taste with your choice of sweetener and add the cinnamon if using. Make the pastry in the usual way. If using barley flour, you shouldn't have any problems rolling it out as it handles very much like ordinary pastry. Makes two 8" diameter pies. I usually brush the tops with filtered water and sprinkle with raw cane sugar but you

could leave them plain if you wish or brush with milk if you prefer. Bake in a moderate oven for around twenty minutes. For a change, try apple and blackberry or plum filling instead.
Serves 4-6 people.

CREME BROULEE (DAY ONE)

* 2lbs (800 grams) Fruits of your choice from the day's list
* Creme Frais or Fromage Frais
* Raw Cane Sugar

Arrange your chosen prepared fruits in an ovenproof dish, sprinkle with sugar if necessary. Spread enough creme frais or fromage frais over the top to completely cover, scatter a thick layer of raw cane sugar over it and put under a hot grill until the sugar is melted and bubbling. Allow to cool before serving.
Serves 4-6 people.

OCCASIONAL TREATS (DAY ONE)

JAM TARTS

* 8oz (200 grams) Wholemeal, Rye or Barley Flour
* 4oz (100 grams) Butter
* 1 level teaspoonful Cream of Tartar
* ½ level teaspoonful Bicarbonate of Soda
* Filtered Water to bind
* 1lb (400 grams) Strawberry, Damson, Apricot, Peach, Plum, Quince or Blackberry Jam (either sweetened with raw cane sugar or sugar free)

Make pastry, roll and cut out the tarts in the usual way. About a teaspoonful of jam is enough for each tart as they tend to boil over in the oven if you overfill them. Bake in a moderate oven for about ten minutes. Serve with cream or creme frais if liked and tolerated. Makes 20-24 tarts.

STICKY BONFIRE TOFFEE (DAY ONE)

* 2oz (50 grams) Plain Chocolate
* 12oz (300 grams) Muscovado Sugar
* 2oz (50 grams) Unsalted Butter
* 14oz (350 grams) Whipping Cream
* Vanilla Pod (from Day Four so don't use again until next true rotation day)

Bring all the ingredients to the boil in a heavy bottomed saucepan. Reduce heat but continue to boil until a small amount dropped into cold water forms a soft ball when rolled between the fingers. Take out the vanilla pod. Beat the toffee until it has lost its shine. Pour into a buttered dish and allow to cool before cutting up into squares. For a firmer toffee, just boil the mixture a while longer until a little dropped into cold water has reached the desired consistency.
Warning:
At the risk of stating the obvious, please don't attempt to make this if there are small children in the kitchen. Boiling sugar is way above the temperature of boiling water and sticks to the skin, burning deep into the tissues, so please take great care and always keep the pan at the back of the cooker out of harm's way. It's as well to have a bowl of iced water nearby in case of splashes, but with reasonable precautions there should be no problems.

FRUIT JUICE ICE LOLLIES

* Freshly juiced fruits of your choice from day's list (or purchased fruit juice of the day if preferred)
* Little powdered vitamin C to prevent discolouration

Simply pour the juice along with some of the pulp for added fibre content into moulds and freeze for at least twelve hours before serving. You will probably find it easier to make up batches with different fruits for different days and freeze them all at the same time and rotate them as required.

CHOCOLATE CARAMEL SHORTCAKE BARS (DAY ONE)

For the Shortbread Base:

* 12 oz (300 grams) Wholemeal, Rye or Barley Flour
* 8oz (200 grams) Butter
* 4oz (100 grams) Raw Cane Sugar

Caramel Topping:

* 8oz (200 grams) Butter or Sunflower Margarine
* 4oz (100 grams) Raw Cane Sugar
* 14 oz Can Condensed Milk
* 3-4 Tablespoons Golden Syrup (Raw Cane)

Chocolate Toping

* 4oz (100 grams) Melted Milk or Plain Chocolate.

Place the shortbread ingredients into a large mixing bowl and rub in until the mixture joins together in a solid lump. Press out into a greased tin 9" x 12" and bake in a moderate oven until golden brown. Allow the shortbread to cool completely in the tin. Meanwhile, combine all the ingredients for the caramel topping in a thick bottomed saucepan and bring gently to the boil stirring constantly to prevent it burning to the bottom. Reduce the heat and continue to stir until the mixture is thick and golden brown. Pour over the cooled shortbread. Once the mixture is set and cooled completely, pour over the melted chocolate.

Please Note:

If you are allergic to nuts, don't use cooking chocolate for this recipe as the cocoa butter will have been removed and replaced with hydrogenated palm kernel oil and this may provoke a reaction. The emulsifier E322 - Lecithin, when added to chocolate, enables the manufacturers to reduce the amount of cocoa butter in the finished product. Lecithin is present in all living cells and is a significant constituent of nerve and brain tissues, however, most commercial lecithin is obtained from soya beans. Other sources are egg yolk and leguminous seeds, including peanuts. I know of at least two nut allergy sufferers who get a strong reaction to it so please be wary and read labels carefully just to be safe. I'd rather be accused of scaremongering than risk making someone ill. Other foods E322 maybe added to are: Powdered Milk, Soft Margarine, Confectionery, Dessert Mixes, Packet trifle Mixes, Vermicelli, Yoghurt Whip, Chocolate Biscuits, Popcorn, Ice Cream and Bakery products.

SODA BREAD (DAY ONE)

* 9oz Wholemeal, Rye or Barley Flour
* 6oz Butter or 5 fluid oz Rapeseed Oil
* 4 Guinea Fowl Eggs
* 1 Rounded Teaspoon Cream of Tartar
* 1 Level Teaspoon Bicarbonate of Soda
* Filtered Water or Cow's Milk

If using oil instead of butter, beat the eggs into it and add the rest of the ingredients. Otherwise method is as follows:
Sift all dry ingredients and rub in butter until like breadcrumbs. Add the eggs and enough filtered water or milk to make a fairly stiff dropping consistency. Transfer to a greased loaf tin and bake in a cool to moderate oven until firm and golden brown. You may need to cover the tin with greaseproof paper to prevent it burning on the outside before it's baked through to the centre.

APPLE AND CINNAMON MUFFINS (OR BASIC CAKE)

* 9oz Wholemeal, Rye, Barley or Maize Flour
* 1 Rounded Dessertspoon or Cornflour
* 6oz Sunflower Margarine or Butter
* 1 Rounded Teaspoon Cream of Tartar
* 1 Level Teaspoon Bicarbonate of Soda
* 2 Dessert Apples
* Apple Juice
* Cinnamon (to taste)

Peel and core apples and whiz in a blender with enough apple juice to make a thick puree. Sift all dry ingredients and rub in the margarine to form breadcrumbs. Add the apple puree with enough extra juice to make a good dropping consistency. Divide the mixture between buncases to make muffins or transfer to two 8" round greased cake tins. Bake in a moderate oven until firm and golden brown. If making as a cake, cover with greaseproof paper for the last ten minutes of baking time to prevent the cake burning on the outside before it's done in the middle.

APPLE AND BLACKBERRY MUFFINS

As above but omit the cinnamon and add 8oz (200 grams) blackberries instead.

OIL CHOCOLATE CAKE (DAY ONE)

* 6oz (150 grams) Wholemeal, Rye or Barley Flour
* 2 Tablespoonful Cocoa Powder
* 1 Heaped Teaspoonful Cream of Tartar
* 1 Level Teaspoonful of Bicarbonate of Soda
* 5oz (125 grams) Raw Cane Sugar
* 2 Tablespoonful of Treacle
* 1½ Heaped Dessertspoonful of Cornflour
* 5 Fluid oz of rapeseed Oil
* 5 fluid oz of Cow's Milk or Filtered Water

Grease and flour 2 x 7" round cake tins. Sift all dry ingredients into a mixing bowl. Gently warm the milk or water, treacle and oil and once the treacle is melted, add to the dry ingredients and blend until smooth. Divide the mixture between the two cake tins and bake in a moderate oven for about fifteen minutes until the cakes are firm and springy to the touch and have shrunk away from the sides of the tins.

FLAPJACKS (DAY ONE)

* 4oz (100 grams) Butter
* 2oz (50 grams) Raw Cane Sugar
* 1 Tablespoonful of Treacle
* 6oz (150 grams) Rolled Oats

Melt butter, treacle and sugar together in a heavy saucepan. Add the oats and mix thoroughly. Press into a greased baking tray, 8" square and bake for approximately 15 minutes until pale golden brown. Mark into squares and allow to cool before lifting off the tray.

STRAWBERRY DAIRY ICE CREAM (DAY ONE)

* 1lb of Strawberries
* Raw Cane Sugar (to taste)
* 2 Tablespoonful of Icing Sugar
* 1 Pint of Whipping Cream
* ½ Pint Extra Thick Double Cream
* 1 Dessertspoonful of Cornflour slaked down with enough filtered water to mix to a smooth paste.

Stew the strawberries with enough filtered water to just cover the bottom of the pan. Add raw cane sugar to taste. Once stewed, add the cornflour mixture and heat until it thickens. Allow to cool and blend in a blender to a smooth puree. When cold add the extra thick double cream and blend again. Meanwhile whisk the whipping cream until stiff. Add the strawberry cream and blend the two together. Turn into an ice cream tub and freeze for an hour or so. Take out and thoroughly whisk again before freezing until required.

WHOLEMEAL, BARLEY OR RYE BREAD

* 3lb (1.5Kilos) Wholemeal, Barley or Rye Flour
* 2oz Fresh Yeast, (or 1 Sachet dried)
* Handful Salt
* 1 Tablespoon Molasses or Raw Cane Sugar
* Approx Pint and a half of Luke Warm Filtered Water

Mix together the yeast, sugar or molasses with about a pint of the water, place the flour in a large bowl and make a well in the centre. Pour in the yeast mixture, allow it to start working before you begin to knead it. You also need to pour the salt around the top of your well making sure at this stage that it doesn't come into contact with the yeast or it will kill it and your bread will not rise. Once you begin the kneading process you can start adding the rest of the water a bit at a time so that it doesn't become too sticky. Starting from the centre of the well gradually bring in more and more flour, mixing in the salt as you go until you have a firm dough that leaves the side of the bowl as you knead it. Continue to knead it for about fifteen minutes before covering with a cloth and leaving in a warm place to rise. Once doubled in size divide the dough into pieces and knead either into small rolls, baps or loaves. Put to rise again until doubled in size, bake in a fairly hot oven until golden brown and they should sound 'hollow' when tapped.

Note:

Barley and rye flours have far less gluten than wheat flour and so will not rise as much. They may even collapse if left to rise for too long before baking.

CHAPTER FIVE

DRINKS FOR DAY TWO

Black Indian or China Tea
Mate Tea
Fennel Tea
Hot Carob with Soya Milk
Filtered or Mineral Water
Grape Juice
Pineapple Juice
Mango Juice
Tomato Juice

The juices should be very well diluted and taken as an occasional treat rather than on a regular basis.

Still or Sparkling Mineral Water

BREAKFAST FOR DAY TWO

Pigs' Liver, Kidneys, Black Pudding and Bacon
Choice of Fruits of the day
Gram Flour Pancakes with Maple Syrup
Pineapple Fritters (with Gram Flour)
Tapioca Pudding With Soya Milk

SOUP/STARTERS FOR DAY TWO

Moules Mariniere (Mussel Soup)
Oyster Soup
Angels on Horseback
Split Pea and Lentil Soup (Vegetarian)

LUNCHES/MAIN MEALS FOR DAY TWO

Roast Pork/Wild Boar
Panfried Pork Steaks/Wild Boar Steaks
Pork and Bean Casserole
Gammon and Pineapple
Mixed Grill of Pig's Liver, Kidneys, Black Pudding, Pork Chops and Bacon
Venison Casserole
Pan Fried Salmon with Cashew Nuts, Parsley and Coriander
Cod Roes
Grilled Pollack, Hake or Cod with Green Beans
Clam Stir Fry
Pot Roast Pheasant
Tofu and Lima Bean Salad, (Vegetarian)
Layered Lentil Loaf (Vegetarian)
Oven Baked Quail
Octopus Stir Fry

DESSERTS FOR DAY TWO

Mango, Pineapple, Grape and Passionfruit Salad
Mango & Tofu Dessert
Pineapple & Tofu Dessert
Pineapple Fritters
Tapioca Pudding with Soya Milk
Fruit Jelly made with Fruit Juices of the Day and Agar, Vegegel or Gelozone

SNACKS/OCCASIONAL TREATS

Sunita Halva (Made with Sesame Seeds and Grape Juice, no additives and available in many health food stores)
Cashew Nuts and Dates
Pineapple Fritters
Gram Flour Pancakes with Maple Syrup
Carob Fruit Juice Jellies

BREAKFASTS FOR DAY TWO

Pig's Liver, Kidneys & Bacon with Black Pudding (grilled or fried)
Choice of Fruits of The Day

PINEAPPLE FRITTERS

Mix some gram (chickpea) flour to a smooth batter with filtered water. Drain some pineapple rings (in own juice) Pat dry and dip in the batter. Leave them to soak in it for a few minutes as you heat some mild olive, grapeseed, or sesame oil in a wok. When the oil is smoking gently dip in the fritters and fry for a few minutes each side until golden brown and crisp. Drain on unbleached kitchen paper before serving.

GRAM FLOUR PANCAKES

Make a batter as for the fritters and make pancakes in the usual way. Serve with maple syrup, soya milk or soya yoghurt, if liked and your choice of fruits of the day.

TAPIOCA PUDDING

(See Page 75)

SOUPS/STARTERS FOR DAY TWO

MOULES MARINIERE (MUSSEL SOUP)

* 1½ pints Fish stock (made from filtered water, heads, tails, bones, bouquet garni of herbs of the day and sea salt)
* 1 Small Glass Dry White Wine (if tolerated and Organic preferably)
* 5-6 Sticks of chopped Celery
* 1 Bulb of Fennel Chopped
* Fennel Seeds (to taste)
* Celery Seeds (to taste)
* Fenugreek Seeds (to taste)
* Bring to the boil and simmer for 20 minutes
* 1oz (25 grams) Soya Margarine
* ½oz (13 grams) Arrowroot Flour

Melt the Soya margarine in a heavy bottomed saucepan. Stir in the arrowroot and cook together to form a roux. Strain some of the fish stock into the roux and blend until smooth. Add the rest of the strained fish stock and stir until it boils again. Remove from the heat. Meanwhile, wash and scrub a quart of mussels. Put them into another pan with a couple of glasses of dry white wine if tolerated or some reserved fish stock if you prefer. Cover and bring to the boil and shake over the heat for about five minutes. Strain the liquor into the soup. 'Beard' the mussels but leave them in a half shell and put them in the soup and reheat before serving with a sprinkling of freshly chopped parsley and coriander.
Serves 4-6 people.

Mussels live on rocks and sandbanks around the coasts of Britain and Northern Europe. Like all shellfish they should be eaten as fresh as possible as they can be a source of acute food poisoning.

They are sold by quart measure rather than by weight and must be tightly closed before cooking. Examine them closely during the first thorough rinsing in cold salted water. Any that are slightly open should be tapped sharply on the work top. If they don't close in response, discard them as they are probably dead and starting to decay. Scrub the remaining mussels well. Rinse again before soaking them in fresh water. Once thoroughly clean, transfer them to a large pan ready for cooking. Some people are happy to eat the beard, the slightly gristly ring which surrounds the mussel. It's a fiddly job to take off all the top half shells and beards so you may prefer to let each person do their own at the table. For **OYSTER SOUP** use the same recipe as above but substitute the mussels for oysters. These need to be treated in pretty much the same way if used fresh. As the saying goes, only buy when there's an 'R' in the month This is not because they may be bad for you at other times. It's merely that the oysters are breeding in spring and early summer and it helps to conserve stocks if they are not caught at this time. You may find it easier to buy tinned ones and chop them up adding them and their liquor to the soup and boiling it for a further few minutes. Serve garnished with freshly chopped parsley and coriander.

ANGELS ON HORSEBACK

* Allow 2 Oysters Per Person
* 2 Rashers of Bacon Per Person

Canned oysters are far quicker and much more convenient to use, as fresh ones are only in season from September to April. Wrap the oysters in the bacon rashers and secure each one with a fine metal skewer. Grill for 4-6 minutes and serve with vegetables and sprouted seeds of your choice from day's list. Garnish with fresh parsley and coriander.

SPLIT PEA AND LENTIL SOUP (DAY TWO) WITH VEGETARIAN OPTION

* 4oz (100 grams) Brown Lentils
* 4oz (100 grams) Yellow Split Peas (soaked overnight)
* 4oz Butter Beans (soaked overnight)
* 1 Onion finely chopped (taken from Day One so miss next rotation then rotate as normal)
* 2 -2½ Pints Vegetable Stock
* Pinch Nutmeg or a little Mace if liked
* 2oz (50 grams) Lean Bacon chopped finely (optional)
* 4oz (100 grams) Grated Celeriac
* 3-4 sticks of Celery chopped
* 2 Carrots chopped
* Celery Seeds (to taste)
* Fennel Seeds (to taste)
* Coriander Seeds (to taste)

Soak Lentils and split peas in filtered water overnight. Drain and add vegetable stock. Bring to the boil. Skim if necessary and meanwhile sweat the onions and bacon with the spices (if using) in a separate pan with a little olive oil. When starting to brown, add to the soup and continue to cook until very tender. If the soup is too thin it can be thickened with a little arrowroot mixed to a smooth paste with filtered water and stirred in quickly. Serve with a sprinkling of chopped parsley and coriander. Serves 4-6 people.

LUNCHES/MAIN MEALS (DAY TWO)

ROAST PORK/WILD BOAR

* 2½ - 3lb (1-1.25 kilograms) joint of Pork or Wild Boar
* Olive Oil, Pork Dripping or Lard for basting

If using lard please check for antioxidants BHA and BHT which may give you problems. Score the meat well before basting and roast in a moderate oven for twenty minutes a pound and twenty minutes over until golden brown. Serves 6-8 people.

Wild boar has a wonderful flavour that is subtly different from conventional pork. Try pan-fried wild boar or pork steaks with your choice of vegetables from the day's list and garnish with fresh herbs.

PORK AND BEAN CASSEROLE (DAY TWO)

* 1lb (400 grams) Cubed Lean Pork (or Wild Boar)
* 1 Bulb of Celeriac (cubed)
* 4oz (100 grams) Haricot Beans (soaked overnight)
* 6 Sticks of Celery
* Celery Seeds (to taste)
* Fennel Seeds (to taste)
* 4oz (100 grams) Chickpeas (soaked overnight)
* 2oz (50 grams) Lentils (soaked overnight)
* 4oz (100 grams) Butter Beans (soaked overnight)
* 4oz (100 grams) Red Kidney Beans (soaked overnight)
* 4oz Lima Beans (soaked overnight)
* Vegetable Stock

Brown the pork in olive oil to seal in the juices. Turn into a good sized casserole dish with all the prepared pulses. Add enough vegetable water (stock) to cover and season with celery and fennel seeds and a little coriander seed and cumin if liked.

Cook the casserole in a moderate oven for approximately two hours until the pork is tender and the pulses are done. Add more filtered water or vegetable stock if necessary after the first hour as the pulses soak up quite a bit.

The diced vegetables should be added about thirty minutes before the pork is ready. Serve with roast parsnips, carrots and peas if liked. Serves 4-6 people.

GRILLED GAMMON AND PINEAPPLE

One gammon steak per person brushed with olive or sesame oil, grilled or fried, topped with pineapple and served with choice of vegetables of the day.

GRILLED OR FRIED PIG'S LIVER, KIDNEYS, PORK CHOPS, BACON & BLACK PUDDING

(With choice of day's vegetables)

VENISON CASSEROLE (DAY TWO

* 1lb (400 grams) Cubed Venison
* 1 Bulb Celeriac (diced)
* 5-6 Sticks of Celery (chopped)
* 4oz Butter Beans (100 grams) (Soaked overnight)
* 4oz (100 grams) Kidney Beans (Soaked overnight)
* 4oz (100 grams) Haricot Beans (Soaked overnight)
* Coriander, Fennel and Cumin seeds (to taste)
* Vegetable/Meat Stock

Brown the meat in olive oil to seal in the juices. Turn into a casserole dish with the beans and spices and cover with stock or filtered water. Cook for about one and a half hours topping up the liquid if necessary. Add the celeriac and celery and cook until tender. Serve with your choice of the vegetables of the day.
Serves 4-6 people.

PAN FRIED SALMON WITH CASHEW NUTS PARSLEY AND CORIANDER

* 4 Salmon Steaks
* 4oz (100 grams) Cashew Nuts
* 1oz (25 grams) Sesame Seeds
* 4oz (100 grams) Sprouted Mung Beans

* 4oz (100 grams) Sprouted Chickpeas
* Sesame Oil
* Parsley and Coriander to garnish

Pan fry the salmon steaks for about five minutes each side depending on the thickness of the steaks. Add the rest of the ingredients and toss in the sesame oil until warmed through. Serve garnished with herbs and your choice of vegetables from the day's list. Serves 4 people.

COD ROES

Cod roes are both cheap and nutritious and are available throughout the winter months until around early April time. Cut them into thick slices and fry them in olive or sesame oil until golden brown, garnish either with coriander or parsley and serve with your choice of vegetables from the day's list.

POLLACK/HAKE OR COD WITH GREEN BEANS (DAY TWO)

* 1 good sized Fish Fillet or Steak Per Person
* Olive or Sesame Oil
* Choice of Herbs of the Day to Garnish

Brush the fish with oil and place under a moderate grill skin side uppermost to start with, turning once, cook for a few minutes each side depending on the thickness of the fish. Serve garnished with choice of herbs of the day, roast parsnips, braised celeriac, or peas with a sprinkling of sprouted pulses, cashew nuts and sesame seeds if liked and tolerated.

CLAM STIR FRY (DAY TWO)

* 1lb (400 grams) Fresh Clams (sliced into two or three pieces depending on size, reserve corals and freeze for adding to oyster or mussel soup)
* 4oz (100 grams) Mung Beans (sprouted)
* 4oz (100 grams) Chickpeas (sprouted)

* 4oz (100 grams) Lima Beans (soaked overnight and precooked)
* 4oz (100 grams) Grated Celeriac
* 5-6 Sticks Celery (chopped finely)
* 1 Bulb of Fennel (chopped finely)
* Choice or Coriander, Celery, Fennel, Caraway, or Cumin Seeds, (to taste)
* Cashew Nuts and Sesame Seeds (optional)
* Coriander Leaves and Parsley to garnish
* Olive or Sesame Oil to stir fry

Heat the oil of your choice in a wok. Add the sliced clams and cook for a minute or so before adding the rest of the ingredients. Heat through and serve with the herb garnish. Serves 4 people.

POT ROAST PHEASANT (DAY TWO)

* 1 Good sized Pheasant
* Strips of Bacon for basting
* 4 Large Parsnips (peeled and quartered lengthways)
* 1 Small Bulb of Celeriac (diced)
* Caraway and Sesame Seeds (optional to taste)
* 1 Glass Dry White Wine (optional)
* Little Vegetable Stock to moisten during cooking
* Olive or Sesame Oil
* Coriander Leaves to garnish and your choice of vegetables from the day's list. Serves 4-6 people.

Place the pheasant in a roasting dish and cover the breast of the bird with bacon strips. Pour some olive or sesame oil over it with a little vegetable stock or white wine to stop the bird becoming too dry during cooking. Cook in a moderate oven, basting frequently, until brown and tender. Half an hour before the bird is ready, add the prepared vegetables of your choice from the day's list and more stock, or white wine if necessary. Serve garnished with coriander leaves. Serves 4-6 people.

LAYERED LENTIL LOAF (DAY TWO) VEGETARIAN

* 8oz (200 grams) Cooked Brown Lentils
* 8oz (200 grams) Ground Cashew Nuts
* 4oz (100 grams) Grated Celeriac
* 4oz (100 grams) Cooked Red Kidney Beans
* 4oz (100 grams) Cooked Butter Beans
* Ground Coriander Seeds (to taste)
* Cumin Seeds (to taste)
* Fennel Seeds (to taste)
* 2 Tablespoons Arrowroot slaked with Filtered Water
* 4-5 Sticks of Celery
* 3-4 Carrots (sliced)
* 1oz (25 grams) Sesame Seeds
* Little Olive or Sesame Oil for frying

Boil the lentils briskly in filtered water until tender. Like all pulses, lentils contain LECTIN which can have a similar effect on the lining of your bowel as gluten has on a Coeliac sufferer. Boiling the lentils briskly until cooked destroys lectin whereas simmering gently until cooked does not. Once the lentils are soft, add the arrowroot, it should thicken almost immediately. Add the ground nuts, spices and grated celeriac and remove from the heat and season to taste. Grease a large loaf tin with olive or sesame oil. Cut a piece of greaseproof paper to fit and line the bottom of the tin. Put in alternate layers of lentil mixture, cooked beans, celery and chopped carrots.

Finish with a final layer of lentils, cover with foil and bake in a moderate oven for at least an hour until firm and golden brown. Serve with choice of vegetables and herbs from the day's list, and a sprinkling of sprouted chickpeas, mung beans and raw sesame and caraway seeds. Serves 4-6 people.

OVEN BAKED QUAIL (DAY TWO)

* Allow 2 Quails Per Person
* 2 Rashers of Bacon Per Person

For the Stuffing: (between 2 quail)

* Large handful chopped Coriander Leaves
* Handful chopped Parsley
* 4oz (100 grams) Ground Cashew Nuts
* 1oz (25 grams) Sesame Seeds
* 4oz (100 grams) Grated Celeriac Root
* 4oz (100 grams) Cooked Butter Beans (lightly mashed)
* 2-3 Sticks of Celery (finely chopped)

Blend together all the ingredients for the stuffing. Divide equally between the birds. Rinse out the cavities with salted water before stuffing loosely. Any spare stuffing can be baked on a greased tray. Put the bacon rashers over the birds' breasts and place in a roasting dish. Baste with either olive or sesame oil and cook in a moderate oven until they are golden brown and tender, basting frequently during cooking. Serve with your choice of herbs and vegetables from the day's list, such as roast parsnips, celeriac, butter beans, green beans, peas, raw celery or carrots.

STIR FIRED OCTOPUS (DAY TWO)

* 12oz (300 grams) Pre-Boiled Octopus (cut into fine strips)
* 4oz (100 grams) Sprouted Chickpeas
* 4oz (100 grams) Sprouted Mung Beans
* 4oz (100 grams) Cooked Lima Beans
* 2oz (50 grams) Sprouted Lentils (optional)
* 4oz (100 grams) Fresh or Frozen Peas
* 4oz (100 grams) Raw Cashew Nuts
* 4oz (100 grams) Grated Celeriac
* 2-3 Carrots (cut into Julienne Sticks)
* 2-3 Sticks of Celery (chopped)
* 1oz (25 grams) Sesame Seeds
* Freshly chopped Coriander and Parsley (to taste)
* Cumin, Mace and Caraway Seeds (to taste)
* Olive or Sesame Oil for frying

I have a Portuguese friend who recommends freezing the octopus prior to cooking it, as the freezing process breaks the fibres and makes the fish more tender. After defrosting, boil the cleaned fish for at least an hour until tenderised, before cutting into strips for stir frying. Heat the oil in a wok or heavy frying pan, and put in the strips of octopus a few at a time until they are all in separately and not stuck together in a heap. Allow them to cook for a couple of minutes before adding the rest of the ingredients. Heat everything through stirring constantly and cook for another couple of minutes before serving. Serves 4-6 people.

TOFU AND LIMA BEAN SALAD VEGETARIAN (DAY TWO)

* 8oz (200 grams) Cooked Lima Beans
* 4-5 Sticks of Celery (chopped)
* 8oz (200 grams) Mixed Nuts - Peanuts, Cashews Pistachios
* 1 Block of Firm Tofu (cubed)
* 2oz (50 grams) Sesame Seeds
* 1 Small Bulb of Celeriac (finely diced or grated)
* 4oz (100 grams) Cooked Kidney Beans
* 4oz (100 grams) Sprouted Mung Beans
* 4oz (100 grams) Sliced Raw Green Beans
* 4oz (100 grams) Sprouted Chickpeas
* Handful Alfalfa Sprouts
* 6 Boiled and sliced Quail's Eggs (optional)
* Few Pitted Olives (Optional)

For the Dressing:

- Few springs Coriander, Parsley and Lovage (chopped finely)
* Pinch (to taste) of Coriander, Fennel and Fenugreek Seeds
* Olive or Sesame Oil

Mix dressing ingredients together and marinade for an hour. Roll tofu cubes in sesame seeds and fry in sesame oil until golden brown. Toss with the rest of the ingredients in a salad bowl, pour over the dressing and serve. Serves 4-6 people.

CASSAVA

These long tubers belong to the same food family as tapioca but they taste very much like potatoes. The best place to find them is your nearest city market where they are popular with many Asian, Chinese and West Indian customers. They are best cut into sections and then peeled to remove the outer brown waxy skin and the smooth inner pink one. They can then be boiled in filtered water as you would cook new potatoes, or roasted in the oven around a joint of meat.

DESSERTS FOR DAY TWO

MANGO, GRAPE AND PASSIONFRUIT SALAD

* 2 Fresh Mangoes
* 1 Fresh Pineapple
* 3/4lb (300 grams) Seedless Grapes
* 2 Passion Fruit
* Handful of Sweet Cicely (finely chopped, optional)
* 1 Stick of fresh Angelica (finely chopped, optional)

Peel slice and cube the mangoes and pineapple. Cut the passionfruit into segments. Place in a large bowl with the rest of the fruit and serve with an optional topping of chopped, lightly roasted, cashew nut and pistachios if liked and tolerated. Serves 4-6 people.

FRUIT JUICE JELLY (DAY TWO)

* 18 fl oz (500 ml) Mango, Grape or Pineapple Juice
* 1 Sachet of Vegegel, Gelozone or Agar Crystals

Put the fruit juice into a saucepan and sprinkle on the gelling agent, whisk in well and heat gradually to near boiling stirring continuously. Remove from the heat and pour into a jelly mould, allow to cool completely before chilling in the fridge for two hours before serving. Serves 4 people.

CAROB COATED FRUIT JELLIES

Your choice of fruit from the day's list, stewed and sweetened to taste with fructose and strained if necessary to form a thick pulp. For every cupful of fruit pulp you need a good tablespoonful of agar gel. Measure out your ingredients into a heavy saucepan and boil quite rapidly for around five minutes until the agar crystals have completely dissolved. Pour out into an oiled baking tray. Allow to set completely before cutting into squares or diamonds and dipping in melted carob. Place on greaseproof paper and allow to set.

Sunita Halva with sultanas and sweetened with grape juice, is an acceptable treat for day two. As are cashew nuts as well as other fruits and nuts of the day.

HOMEMADE SOYA YOGHURT WITH CHOICE OF FRUITS OF THE DAY AND SWEETENED WITH MAPLE SYRUP

(See basic yoghurt recipe on day one, it can also be used for sheep and goat's milk yoghurt as used on day 3)

PINEAPPLE & TOFU DESSERT

Use one large or two small tins of pineapple in their own juice. Put in a blender with a small block of tofu and blend until smooth. Serves 2.

MANGO & TOFU DESSERT

As above but use two large tins of mangoes, pour off the syrup and use either grape or pineapple juice instead.

TAPIOCA PUDDING WITH SOYA MILK (DAY TWO)

* 500 mls Soya Milk (fortified with calcium)
* 2oz Tapioca
* Maple Syrup (to taste)

Put the tapioca in a heavy saucepan with the soya milk and bring slowly to the boil stirring constantly. A flat wooden spatula seems to work best as it helps to stop the tapioca sticking to the bottom of the pan. Reduce the heat and continue to simmer until the tapioca softens and starts to go transparent. Add the maple syrup to taste and serve. Serves 3-4 portions.

CHAPTER SIX

DRINKS FOR DAY THREE

Sage or Lemon Balm Tea
Comfrey or Peppermint Tea
Camomile Tea
Prewitt's Chicory
Dandelion Coffee
Ground, Decaffeinated Coffee with Sheep or Goat's Milk
& Beet Sugar
Filtered or Mineral Water

BREAKFASTS FOR DAY THREE

Millet Porridge with Sheep, Goat's or Rice Milk
Cornflakes with Sheep, Goat's or Rice Milk
Rice Krispies with Sheep, Goat's or Rice Milk
Grilled Lamb's Liver and Kidneys with Mushrooms and Fresh herbs
Live Sheeps' or Goats' Milk Yoghurt with choice of
Fruits of the Day
(Sweetened with Honey or Beet Sugar)
Choice of Fruit of the Day, Feta or Goat's Cheese
Boiled, Fried, Poached or Scrambled Eggs
Omelette with Mushrooms and Herbs
Oak Smoked Mackerel and Wild Rice Kedgeree
Maize (Polenta) Pancakes

SOUPS/STARTERS FOR DAY THREE

Fig and Walnut Salad with Feta or Goat's Cheese (Vegetarian)
'Left Overs Soup'
Mushroom Soup
Deep Fried Whitebait

LUNCHES/MAIN MEALS FOR DAY THREE

Grilled Dab or Flounder

Roast Partridge with Fig and Walnut Stuffing
Mushroom, Cheese or Herb Omelette, (Vegetarian)
Goat's Meat Joint with Rosemary, Thyme and Basil
Roast Chicken with Thyme and Sage
Pan-Fried Chicken with Mushroom and Herb Sauce
Lamb's Liver with Basil, Oregano and Mushrooms
Grilled Lamb's Liver and Kidney Kebabs
Grilled Mackerel with Herbs, Mushroom and Spinach Stuffing
Grilled Plaice or Sole
Crab or Lobster Salad
Grilled, Panfried or Barbecued Lamb Cutlets with Mint, Basil & Rosemary
Salsify in a Creamy Cheese and Tarragon Sauce
Stuffed Globe Artichokes Vegetarian
Sardines or Pilchards with Wild Rice, Mushroom and Spinach Salad
Baked or Boiled Yams

DESSERTS FOR DAY THREE

Choice of Stewed Fruits of the Day
Figs, Pomegranates, Lychees, Mulberries
Figs or Lychees in Sheep's or Goat's Milk Yoghurt, Sweetened with Honey

SNACKS/OCCASIONAL TREATS FOR DAY THREE

Figs, Walnuts, Pecans, Choice of Fruits of the Day
Steamed Fig & Honey Pudding
Coffee Pudding
White Sauce
Rice Pudding
Ground Rice Pudding
Millet Flan Jacks
Fig & Walnut Cake
Egg-free Fig & Walnut Cake

BREAKFASTS (DAY THREE)

GRILLED LAMB'S LIVER WITH KIDNEYS, MUSHROOMS AND FRESH HERBS

Skin and cure the kidneys and rinse well. Brush the liver and kidneys with walnut oil or dripping and place under a medium hot grill and cook until tender. Meanwhile, peel and chop the mushrooms and fry in very little dripping or walnut oil in a frying pan. Serve the whole lot garnished with fresh herbs of the day if liked.

SHEEP' OR GOATS' MILK YOGHURT (DAY THREE)

Make the yoghurt at least twenty-four hours before needed using the method given on day one for cow's milk yoghurt. The culture used should not cause any problems as this type of friendly bacteria normally inhabits the intestines and keeps down the growth of unfriendly parasites like Candida Albicans. Sweeten the yoghurt to taste with honey and serve with your choice of fruits of the day.

BOILED, FRIED, SCRAMBLED OR POACHED EGGS OR MUSHROOM AND HERB OMELETTE

(Cooked in the usual ways)

OAK SMOKED MACKEREL AND WILD RICE KEDGEREE

* 2 Fillets of Mackerel (cooked and flaked)
* 2 Hard Boiled Eggs (diced)
* 8oz (200 grams) Cooked Wild Rice
* 4oz Feta or Goat's Cheese (grated)
* 4oz Mushrooms (sliced)
* 2oz (50 grams) Sweetcorn
* Freshly Chopped Tarragon and Basil (to taste)
* Sunflower or Sunflower Oil

Cook the eggs, fish and the rice the night before to save time. Then next morning fry the mushrooms in a little oil. Add sweetcorn, rice, fish and diced eggs and warm through sprinkle over the cheese and herbs and continue to cook until cheese starts to melt and serve. Enough for 3-4 people.

MILLET PORRIDGE

* 1 Cup of Millet Flakes
* 4-5 Cups of either Filtered Water, Sheep or Goats' Milk, Rice Milk or Millet milk
* Beet Sugar or Honey to taste

Put all ingredients into a saucepan and bring to the boil stirring constantly. Serve either on its own or with figs and lychees.

POLENTA (MAIZE FLOUR) PANCAKES

* 2 Tablespoonful Maize Flour
* 2 Tablespoonful Brown Rice Flour
* 2 Free Range Eggs
* Filtered Water
* Sunflower or Safflower Oil

Add the eggs to the flours and make a batter and fry pancakes in the usual way. Makes 3-4 pancakes. Serve with honey, figs or lychees. For a savoury version try mushrooms with spinach and grated feta or goat's cheese with a sprinkling of fresh herbs from day's list.

SOUPS/STARTERS (DAY THREE)

WALNUT & FETA CHEESE SALAD

* 8oz (200 grams) Walnuts
* 4oz (200 grams) Mixed Pecans, Butternuts and Hickory Nuts
* 8oz (200 grams) Raw Mushrooms (well washed, peeled and sliced)
* 8oz (200 grams) Beetroot (freshly boiled, cooled and diced)
* 12oz (300 grams) Feta or Goat's Cheese (cubed)
* 8oz Dried Figs (soaked overnight and roughly chopped)

* Large handful of freshly chopped mixed herbs, (Sweet Basil, Pineapple, Sage, Lemon Balm, Applemint and Marjoram make a lovely combination but you can use whichever you prefer from the day's list.
* Walnut Oil

Mix some of the herbs with the oil and leave to marinade in the fridge for about an hour. Toss the rest of the ingredients together in a salad bowl, pour over the dressing and serve. Serves 6-8 people.

LEFT OVERS SOUP

Any juices from the day's meat can be combined with left over vegetables and the water they were cooked in and whizzed together in a blender to form a tasty and nourishing soup. Freeze until needed on rotation. Pour off any fat from the roasting dish, being careful not to pour out the juices as well. Rinse out the dish with hot vegetable water to obtain the maximum amount of stock. If there are insufficient ingredients for a batch of soup, don't worry. Blend and freeze what you have and use it as a base for fresh soup on the required day.

MUSHROOM SOUP (DAY THREE) - WITH VEGETARIAN OPTION)

* 1lb (400grams) of Flat Mushrooms (well washed and chopped fairly small)
* 2 Pints of Vegetable/Chicken Stock
* Lamb Dripping or Walnut Oil
* Large Handful of Fresh Spinach (chopped)
* Fresh Basil (to taste)
* Fresh Oregano (to taste)
* Live Sheep or Goat's Milk Yoghurt (to taste)

Sweat the mushrooms, spinach and herbs in a heavy bottomed saucepan with the oil or lamb dripping to extract as much flavour as possible. Pour in the stock, bring to the boil and reduce the heat. Simmer until the mushrooms are tender. Allow to cool before putting through a blender. Add live sheep or goats' milk yoghurt to taste, reheat and serve with a swirl of yoghurt if liked or with a sprinkling of your favourite herbs from today's list. Serves 4-6 people.

DEEP FRIED WHITEBAIT (DAY THREE)

* 1lb (400 grams) Whitebait
* Walnut Oil

These tiny silver coloured fish are cooked whole. Fry in hot oil for no more than one and a half minutes. Serve with herbs of your choice and walnut oil dressing. Serves 4 people.

STUFFED GLOBE ARTICHOKES

* 4 Large Artichokes
* 2oz (50 grams) Sweetcorn
* 2oz (50 grams) Mushrooms (chopped and fried)
* 4oz (100 grams) Cooked Wild Rice
* Freshly chopped Tarragon (to taste)

Trim off the rough lower leaves of the artichokes and cut off the stalks as close to the flowers as possible so that they will stand upright. Trim off tops of the other leaves with scissors. Put in a pan of boiling, salted, filtered water and simmer for ten to fifteen minutes depending on their size. Drain and plunge into cold water. When cool enough to handle, scoop out and discard the chokes. These are the hairy centres reached by separating the centre leaves of the artichokes. Mix together all the ingredients for the stuffing. Stuff the centres of the artichokes. Stand in a dish, it only needs to be just big enough to hold them all upright. Pour in enough chicken stock to half fill the dish. Cover with a lid or tin foil and bake at 180c or Gas Mark 4 for about forty five minutes. Serves 4.

SALSIFY IN A CREAMY TARRAGON AND CHEESE SAUCE

* 2lb of Salsify
* Fresh Tarragon (to taste)
* 1 Pint of Sheep or Goats' Milk
* 1 Very Heaped Dessertspoonful of Cornflour
* 2oz (50 grams) Feta or Goat's Cheese (Grated)

Scrape the salsify quickly, cut into 2" lengths and plunge into boiling water to prevent discoloration. Simmer for around 20 minutes until tender. Meanwhile, mix the cornflour to a smooth paste with a little of the milk, add the rest of the milk and the cheese then slowly bring to the boil, continue to stir to avoid lumps until the mixture starts to thicken. Add the tarragon and continue to cook until the cheese is melted. Drain the salsify, pour over the sauce, heat through and serve. 4-6 people.

LUNCHES/MAIN MEALS (DAY THREE)

DAB OR FLOUNDER

Dab and flounder are both 'bottom feeders'. In other words they are scavengers who take up a lot of mud as they feed, which impairs the taste. My fishmonger recommends soaking the fish in salted water for one to two hours to bring out the true flavour of the fish, which can then be grilled, baked or fried in the usual way.

ROAST PARTRIDGE WITH FIG AND WALNUT STUFFING

* 2 Good Sized Partridges
* 8oz (200 grams) Unsulphured Dried Figs (soaked overnight and chopped)
* 8oz (200 grams) Walnuts (chopped)
* 8oz (200 grams) Pecans (chopped)
* Few Sprigs of Basil & Sage (chopped finely)
* Fresh Chopped Thyme (½ teaspoon if using dried)

Wash the birds in salted water, rub a little salt into the cavity before rinsing out. Pat dry with unbleached paper towels. Mix all the ingredients for the stuffing together and divide between the two birds. Baste with walnut oil or lamb dripping and place in a roasting tin. It's advisable to place the birds breast side down for the first half of the cooking time. This allows the juices to flow down into the breast to make it more succulent and moist. Halfway through cooking turn the birds over again and cook until golden and tender. Garnish with herbs and serve with your choice of vegetables of the day. Serves 4-6 people.

OMELETTES

Allow three eggs per person. Whisk the eggs well, if you want to use an electric food mixer you will get much more volume and the eggs will become thick and creamy and almost doubled in size. Heat some walnut oil or lamb dripping in an omelette pan and pour in the eggs. Cook gently on one side then pop under the grill for a couple of minutes until the omelette is well risen and golden. Turn out and serve. Suggested fillings, cooked chicken left overs, mushrooms, Feta or Goats' cheese, herbs of the day and spinach.

ROAST LAMB OR GOAT'S MEAT JOINT WITH ROSEMARY, THYME AND BASIL (DAY THREE)

* 1 Decent sized Joint of Lamb or Goat
* Rosemary, Thyme and Basil (to taste)
* Walnut Oil or Lamb Dripping

Brown the joint over moderate heat to seal in the juices. Place in a roasting tin baste with oil or dripping, and sprinkle the herbs over the meat. If using goats' meat you may find it advisable to add some filtered water to keep it moist and cook it very slowly as it tends to be tougher than lamb. Cover and roast in a moderate oven until tender. Garnish with fresh herbs and serve with your choice of vegetables from the day's list. Serves 4-6 people depending on size of joint.

ROAST CHICKEN WITH THYME AND SAGE (DAY THREE)

* 1 Free Range Chicken
* Thyme and Sage (to taste)
* Sunflower or Safflower Oil

Rub salt around the cavity of the chicken and rinse well. Pat dry with unbleached, plain kitchen paper. Place in a roasting dish and drizzle over the oil. Liberally scatter herbs over the top, cover and roast until golden brown. Serve with choice of vegetables from the day's list. Serves 4-6 people.

PAN-FRIED CHICKEN WITH MUSHROOM AND HERB SAUCE

* 1 Chicken Breast Per Person
* 4oz (100 grams) Flat Mushrooms Per Person
* Fresh Basil and Tarragon to taste
* Live Sheep or Goat's Milk Yoghurt
* Safflower or Sunflower Oil for frying

Pan fry the chicken breasts until golden and tender. Lift out of the pan and keep warm Add the washed and chopped mushrooms to the pan with the herbs and allow to 'sweat' over a low heat to bring out the flavour. Continue cooking gently until the mushrooms start to brown. Add the yoghurt and stir well to make a creamy sauce. (If your sauce starts to curdle or separate, add an egg yolk beaten with a little more yoghurt and stir until the sauce thickens). Pour over the chicken and serve with choice of vegetables from the day's list.

LAMB'S LIVER WITH MUSHROOMS (DAY THREE)

* 1lb (400 grams) Lamb's Liver
* ½ lb (200 grams) Flat Mushrooms
* Basil (to taste)
* Winter Savoury (to taste)
* Filtered Water
* Walnut Oil or Lamb Dripping

Heat the oil or fat in a frying pan. Cut the liver into fairly thin strips and lay the strips of liver in the hot oil, reduce the heat and brown them evenly before adding the mushrooms, winter savoury and basil. Cook for a few more minutes before serving with your choice of vegetables of the day. Serves 4 people.

GRILLED LAMB'S LIVER AND KIDNEY KEBABS (DAY THREE)

* ½lb (200 grams) Lamb's Liver (cut into cubes)
* 1lb (400 grams) Lamb's Kidneys
* ½lb (200 grams) Button Mushrooms
* Rosemary and Thyme (to taste)
* Sunflower Oil

Blanch the kidneys in very hot water for two or three minutes, before plunging them into very cold water. This prevents them from curling during cooking. Skin and core them. Marinade the liver and kidneys for two to three hours in the rosemary, thyme, and oil. Cut the kidneys to roughly the same size as the liver and mushrooms and thread onto metal skewers. Brush with the marinade and grill or barbecue until tender. Garnish with fresh basil and marjoram and serve with choice of vegetables of the day.
Serves 4 people.

GRILLED MACKEREL WITH MUSHROOM AND HERB STUFFING (DAY THREE)

* 4 Mackerel (cleaned and gutted)
* 8oz (200 grams) Mushrooms (cleaned and finely chopped and lightly fried)
* 2oz (50 grams) Walnuts (chopped, optional)
* 2oz (50 grams) Pecans (chopped, optional)
* Lemon Balm and Thyme (to taste)
* Safflower or Sunflower Oil

Combine all the ingredients for the stuffing and mix well. Push a little of the mixture into the cavities of each of the mackerel. Slit the fish two or three times along each side, brush with oil and place under a moderately hot grill and cook for five to seven minutes each side turning once. Serve with choice of vegetables from the day's list. Serves 4 people.

GRILLED PLAICE OR SOLE (DAY THREE)

* Allow 2 Fillets of Fish Per Person
* Freshly Chopped Thyme and Winter Savoury
* Safflower or Sunflower Oil

Put the finely chopped herbs into a bowl with a little oil and allow to stand for a while before brushing the fillets and placing them under a moderate grill. It's best to start them cooking with the skin side uppermost, turning over halfway through the cooking time. Allow three to five minutes each side depending on the thickness of the fish. Serve with your choice of vegetables from the day's list.

SARDINES OR PILCHARDS WITH SPINACH, MUSHROOM AND WILD RICE SALAD (DAY THREE)

* 1 Large Tin Pilchards in Brine or 3 Small Tins Sardines in Brine
* 8oz (200 grams) Fresh Shitake Mushrooms (washed and sliced thinly)
* 8oz (200 grams) Fresh Young Spinach Leaves
* 3-4 Fresh Young Stalks and Leaves of Swiss Chard (chopped finely)
* Handful of Freshly Chopped Orache Leaves - 'Mountain Spinach' (optional)
* 2 Boiled Beetroot (peeled, cooled and diced)
* 8oz (200 grams) Sweetcorn
* 8oz (200 grams) Cooked Brown Rice
* 1 Head of Chicory (shredded)
* 4oz (100 grams) Feta Cheese

*   2 Hard Boiled Free Range Eggs (sliced)
*   4oz (100 grams) Walnuts or Pecans

Toss all salad ingredients together. Make a dressing of sheep or goat's milk yoghurt, add chopped mint leaves with basil to taste. Serves up to 4 people.

Use dressed Crab or Lobster as an alternative to Sardines or Pilchards.

Note: You may want to use tinned crab or lobster in the above recipe but you would need to check the ingredients listed on the label. Most manufacturers seem to add monosodium glutamate to enhance the flavour and sodium metabisulphite as a preservative. Your best bet is to buy a freshly cooked crab or lobster from a good fishmonger who will dress it for you if you ask him. Choose one that feels heavy for its size, this is a good guide to freshness.

PAN-FRIED, GRILLED OR BARBECUED LAMB CUTLETS (DAY THREE)

Cook them in the usual way and garnish with rosemary and mint if liked and tolerated and serve with choice of vegetables from day's list.

Most of the vegetables on today's list are quite easy to grow in your own garden and you may find it easier than trying to get some of them from a supermarket. See the hints and tips section on how to grow them.

BAKED OR BOILED YAMS

Yams can be easily found in many big city markets where they are very popular with Asian and West Indian communities.

Raw yams smell very similar to raw potatoes. The larger varieties with their rough skins can be peeled and boiled in a similar way to potatoes while the smaller, softer varieties can be left whole and wrapped in tin foil and baked in the oven until tender, then split open, sprinkled with grated feta or goat's cheese and chopped herbs. (Lemon balm, applemint and pineapple sage are lovely but you can choose from the day's list)

BREADFRUIT

These look like greenish grey melons on the outside and when halved, the centres are dark in appearance but not heavily seeded like a melon. Market stallholders are happy to sell them in portions rather than having to buy a whole one which may be too much for you. Cut out the dark centre part as this is very bitter. They can be peeled, diced and cooked like potatoes, either steamed or lightly boiled or roasted in the oven with a joint of meat.

OKRA (GUMBO - USA)

These versatile little pods can be steamed, boiled, or eaten raw in salads. They can also be included in soups and stews or in stir fries. To prepare them just top and tail them and chop or leave them whole.

Okra can be grown from seed in an unheated greenhouse, but in our climate it is not warm enough to grow out of doors. Easy to find in your nearest city market.

CHOU-CHOU

This vegetable grows on a tree and looks very much like a green apple. Like the previous vegetables I've mentioned it can usually be found at your nearest city market.

Peel and boil for a short while in filtered water or steam it.

TURIA GINGA

These long ridged vegetables are smaller and thinner than cucumbers to look at. They can be peeled, chopped and added to soups, stews and stir fries with freshly chopped herbs to enhance their flavour.

DESSERTS/OCCASIONAL TREATS (DAY THREE)

STEAMED FIG AND HONEY PUDDING

* 4oz (100 grams) Beet Sugar
* 4oz (100 grams) Maize Meal (Polenta)
* 1 Heaped Teaspoonful Cream of Tartar
* 1 Level Teaspoonful Bicarbonate of Soda
* 1 Heaped Dessertspoonful of Cornflour
* 6 Fluid Oz Sunflower or Safflower Oil
* Approx 6 Dried Figs (unsulphured and soaked overnight)
* 2 Dessertspoonful of Runny Honey

Sift all the dry ingredients together. Add the oils, figs and honey with enough filtered water to make a fairly soft cake mixture consistency. Turn out into a pyrex pudding basin and steam, (using filtered water) for approximately 1 hour until well risen and firm to the touch. Serves 4-6 people.

COFFEE PUDDING

Follow recipe above but leave out the figs and honey and substitute for half a cup of very strong black coffee. Serves 4-6 people.

WHITE SAUCE

* 2oz (50 grams) of Cornflour
* 2oz (50 grams) of Beet Sugar or Honey to taste
* 1 Pint (500 mls) Either Sheep, Goats' or Rice Milk

Mix cornflour and sweetener to a smooth paste with a little of the milk. Add the rest of the milk and bring slowly to the boil stirring constantly until it thickens. Serve on its own or with either of the previous two recipes. For variation, you could add some strong black coffee to go with the coffee pudding.

RICE PUDDING

* 2oz (50 grams) Pudding Rice
* 2oz (50 grams) Beet Sugar or Honey to taste
* 1 Pint (500 mls) Sheep, Goats' or Rice Milk

Put rice and sweetener into a pudding dish. Pour over the milk and stirring well. Put into a cool oven to cook gently for approximately 1½ hours. Remember to stir every 20 minutes or so and top up with more milk if necessary to stop it drying out before it's properly cooked.

GROUND RICE PUDDING

* 2oz (50 grams) Ground Rice
* 2oz (50 grams) Beet Sugar or Honey to taste
* 1 Pint (500 mls) Sheep, Goats' or Rice Milk

Mix rice and sweetener to a smooth paste with a little of the milk. Add rest of the milk and bring gently to the boil stirring constantly until it thickens.
Serves 3-4 people.

MILLET FLAPJACKS

* 4oz (100 grams) Sunflower Margarine (dairy free)
* 2oz (50 grams) Beet Sugar
* 1 Tablespoon of Honey
* 4oz (100 grams) Millet Flakes
* 2oz Brown Rice Sugar

Melt the margarine and honey in a saucepan. Add the rest of the ingredients and turn out into a greased 8" cake tin. Bake in a moderate oven for approx 15 minutes until pale golden brown. Makes 6-8 segments.

FIG AND WALNUT CAKE

* 4oz (100 grams) Maize Flour (Polenta)
* 4oz (100 grams) Brown Rice Flour
* 8oz (200 grams) Beet Sugar
* 8oz (200 grams) Sunflower Margarine (dairy free)
* 4 Free Range Eggs
* 4oz (100 grams) Dried, Unsulphured Figs (soaked for about one hour)
* 4oz (100 grams) Chopped Walnuts or Pecans
* 1 Raised Teaspoonful Cream of Tartar
* 1 Level Teaspoonful of Bicarbonate of Soda

Beat sugar and margarine together. Add eggs one at a time and beat thoroughly. Sift together the flours and raising agents and add to the mixture. Add chopped figs and walnuts and divide mixture between two greased loaf tins. Decorate with more walnuts or pecans and bake in a moderate oven for approximately 30-35 minutes.

EGG-FREE FIG AND WALNUT CAKE

* 4oz (100 grams) Maize Flour (Polenta)
* 4oz (100 grams) Brown Rice Flour
* 8oz (200 grams) Beet Sugar or 6oz (150 grams) Runny Honey
* 8oz (200 grams) Sunflower Margarine (dairy free)
* 1 Raised Dessertspoonful Cornflour
* 4oz (100 grams) Dried Figs (soaked for at least an hour)
* 4oz (100 grams) Chopped Walnuts or Pecans
* 1 Raised Teaspoonful Cream of Tartar
* 1 Level Teaspoonful Bicarbonate of Soda
* Either Rice Milk, Sheep or Goats' Milk or Filtered Water to slake down to cake batter consistency

Sift dry ingredients into a bowl. Add sugar and margarine and rub together until the mixture is like breadcrumbs. Add figs and walnuts then pour in enough filtered water or your choice of milk to get a good cake batter consistency. Bake in a moderate oven for approximately thirty minutes.

FIGS IN SHEEP'S OR GOAT'S YOGHURT (DAY THREE)

Scald dried unsulphured figs and leave to soak overnight in boiled, filtered water. Stew in their liquor with a little honey to taste and serve with either Greek ewe's milk yoghurt or homemade using the method given on day one.

FIGS, POMEGRANATES, LYCHEES, MULBERRIES

CHAPTER SEVEN

DRINKS FOR DAY FOUR

Lemon Verbena Tea
Black or Redcurrant Juice
Cranberry Juice
Coconut Milk

Freshly Juiced Orange, Lemon, Lime or Grapefruit, diluted with Mineral water. Lime or Lemon and Ginger Tea, made with fresh Lime or Lemon slices and Root Ginger and Boiling Filtered Water, sweetened to taste with Fructose, Filtered or Mineral Water

BREAKFASTS FOR DAY FOUR

Stewed Fruits of the Day, Sweetened with Fructose
Buckwheat Pancakes served with choice of Fruits of the Day
Boiled, Scrambled, Poached or Fried Duck Eggs with Saute Potatoes
Duck Egg Omelette with Herbs, Tamarillos, Tomatoes, Aubergines, Peppers
Chillies and Cooked, Diced Potatoes
Fruits of the Day Alone
Saute Potatoes with Fillets of Fish of the Day
Baked Or Sauteed Plantain with Coconut Milk

SOUPS/STARTERS FOR DAY FOUR

Stuffed Peppers with Nuts and Buckwheat Grains (Vegetarian)
Tomato Soup

LUNCHES/MAIN MEALS FOR DAY FOUR

Baked or Pan-Fried Swordfish Steaks
Pan-Fried Shark Steaks
Stir Fried Squid Rings
Grilled Gurnard/Grouper
Steamed Tilapia or Red Snapper
Grilled Sea Bass, Tilapia, Red or Pink Snapper or Sea Bream

Baked or Steamed Red Snapper or Tilapia
Baked Eel Steaks
Duck Egg Omelette with Herbs, Tamarillos, Aubergines, Tomatoes, Peppers
Duck Breasts in an Orange and Ginger Sauce
Baked Rainbow Trout or Red Snapper with Gooseberry Sauce
Roast Turkey with Cranberry or Gooseberry Sauce
Roast Goose with Tomato and Aubergine Stuffing
Hare or Rabbit Casserole
Fish Pie
Pan-Fried Haddock and Chips
Roast Grouse
Roast Duck with Gooseberry Sauce
Scallop Stir Fry with Tomatoes and Aubergines
Roast Woodpigeon

DESSERTS FOR DAY FOUR

Rhubarb and Ginger Crumble
Potato Flour 'Custard' with choice of Fruits of the Day
Buckwheat Pancakes with choice of Fruits of the Day
Fresh Fruit Salad of the Day

SNACKS/OCCASIONAL TREATS FOR DAY FOUR

Choice of Fruits and Nuts of the Day
Basic Cake Mixture
Ginger or Currant cake from above mixture

BREAKFASTS FOR DAY FOUR

BUCKWHEAT PANCAKES WITH DUCK EGGS

* 4oz (100 grams) Buckwheat Flour
* 1 Duck Egg or 1 Heaped Dessertspoonful of Potato Flour
* Little Filtered Water

Combine the buckwheat, egg or potato starch. Add enough filtered water to obtain the correct consistency and make pancakes in the usual way. Serve with fruits of the day.

BOILED, POACHED, SCRAMBLED OR FRIED DUCK EGGS (DAY FOUR)

All cooked in the usual way, try with saute potatoes, or make a duck egg omelette, with choice of herbs of the day, tamarillos, tomatoes, aubergines, chillies and peppers.

SAUTE POTATOES WITH FISH FILLETS (DAY FOUR)

For quickness boil the potatoes the night before, then fry them with your choice of fish fillets from the day's list, in Tomor margarine (made from coconut oil) or hazelnut oil or, if you are allergic to nuts, use an oil of your choice from day two and rotate as usual.

BAKED OR SAUTE PLANTAINS

Either wrap the whole plantain in tin foil and bake for around thirty minutes in a moderate oven, or peel and slice and saute gently in tomor margarine for a few minutes each side until golden and crisp. Serve with a sprinkling of chopped nuts and ginger, if liked and tolerated and topped with thick coconut milk.

FRESH FRUIT SALAD

See recipe in dessert section or stew any fruit of your choice from the day's list.

SOUPS/STARTERS (DAY FOUR)

STUFFED PEPPERS (DAY FOUR) VEGETARIAN

* 1 Pepper Per Person
* Sprouted Buckwheat Grains
* Chopped Nuts of the Day, (Hazels, Brazils, Filberts or Cobnuts)
* 2-3 Tomatoes or Tamarillos (blanched, skinned and chopped)

Cut the tops off the peppers and scoop out the seeds and soft pith. Mix the rest of the ingredients together and fill the cavities. Bake in a moderate oven for about 10 minutes or so depending on their size.

TOMATO SOUP

* 4lb (1600 grams) Frying Tomatoes (blanched, skinned and chopped)
* 2 Pints of Well Flavoured Poultry Stock
* 1lb (400 grams) Potatoes (cut into small dice)
* Paprika Pepper (to taste)
* Cayenne Pepper (to taste)
* 6oz (150 grams) Buckwheat Pasta (optional)

It's difficult to get very ripe tomatoes these days because of new EC regulations on displaying vegetables of a certain standard. However most greengrocers are happy to let you have tomatoes that are past their best for next to nothing if you ask. Blanch and skin them by plunging into boiling water for a couple of minutes and then into cold water. The skins should slide off easily. Chop roughly and put them into a large saucepan, (preferably stainless steel as the acid in the tomatoes will act on the surface of aluminium pans, causing some traces of the metal to leech into the soup). Add the potatoes and stock. Season to taste. Bring to the boil then reduce the heat and simmer until the potatoes are cooked, by which time the tomatoes will be soft and pulpy. Allow to cool and either put through a

blender or juice extractor if you want to get rid of the seeds. Reheat and add the buckwheat pasta, if using and serve.
Serves 6-8 people.

LUNCHES/MAIN MEALS (DAY FOUR)

PAN FRIED SHARK OR SWORDFISH STEAKS

* 1 Shark (Rock Salmon) or Swordfish Steak Per Person
* Little Lime Juice and Zest (to taste)
* Little Root Ginger (to taste)
* Hazelnut or Tomor Margarine (or oil from another day if you cannot tolerate either of these and rotate as usual)

Fry the fish steaks in the oil of your choice for a few minutes each side, turning once. Add lime juice and ginger if using, and serve with jacket potatoes and your choice of vegetables from the day's lists.

STIR FIRED SQUID RINGS (DAY FOUR)

Clean the squids not forgetting to remove the beak (it looks like a small piece of clear plastic) if you ask nicely the fishmonger may do them for you. The squids need to be sliced across the body into rings. Some supermarkets sell them ready prepared nowadays. The oils for today are hazelnut, and palm oil. If allergic to nuts then use an oil from another day. Fry the squids in the oil of your choice for a couple of minutes before adding your choice of the following: chopped peppers, chillis, pimentos, tamarillos (tree tomatoes) aubergines, tomatoes and sorrel or lemon verbena. Add a squeeze of lime juice and zest if liked with a sprinkling of fresh ginger root cut into julienne sticks (matchsticks) cook until squids are tender and serve with new potatoes.

GRILLED GURNARD (DAY FOUR)

Brush with choice of oil of the day (or substitute for another day if you cannot tolerate nuts and rotate as usual) Grill fillets of gurnard for 2 or 3 minutes each side and serve with new potatoes and choice of vegetables of the day.

GRILLED SEA BASS, TILAPIA, RED OR PINK SNAPPER OR SEA BREAM (DAY FOUR)

If cooking the fish on the bone, clean and scale it and put a few slices of tomato into the cavity if liked and tolerated. Make deep cuts along the sides of the fish, brush with your choice of oil and place under a medium hot grill for a few minutes each side depending on the thickness of the fish. Serve with potatoes and choice of vegetables from the day's list.

STEAMED TILAPIA OR RED SNAPPER (DAY FOUR)

Any of the fish from the day's list can be steamed if you wish to. Just clean the fish, rinse out the cavity and scrape off the scales before putting in the steamer. If you wish, you can add a squeeze of fresh lime juice over the fish with a sprinkling of fresh root ginger and a pinch ground cardomon. Steam for around eight minutes or so depending on the size of the fish. Serve with jacket potatoes and choice of vegetables of the day.

BAKED EEL STEAKS (DAY FOUR)

Take one eel steak per person, brush a square of tin foil with hazelnut oil or Tomor margarine. Place the eel steak in the centre and squeeze a little lime juice over it and a scattering of freshly chopped lemon verbena, fold the tin foil over to make a parcel and bake in a moderate oven for about fifteen minutes. Serve with potatoes and your choice of vegetables from the day's list.

DUCK EGG OMELETTE (DAY FOUR) VEGETARIAN

* 3 Duck Eggs Per Omelette
* ½ Red Pepper (de-seeded and sliced)
* ½ Yellow Pepper (de-seeded and sliced)
* 1 Good Sized Tomato (sliced)
* 1 Tamarillo (Tree Tomato - optional - sliced)

* Little Chopped Lemon Verbena (optional)
* Some Chopped Aubergine
* Paprika Pepper (to taste)
* Cooked, Diced Potato

Crack the eggs one at a time into a separate bowl to check for freshness. Beat well and pour into an omelette pan using either poultry fat, hazelnut oil, or Tomor margarine. As mentioned earlier, if you are allergic to nuts but don't want to use poultry fat, use oil from another day and rotate as usual. Add the rest of the ingredients in the omelette and cook in the usual way. Serve with potatoes and choice of vegetables from the day's list.

ROAST DUCK BREASTS WITH ORANGE AND GINGER SAUCE (DAY FOUR)

* 1 Good Sized Duck Breast Per Person
* Little Grated Root Ginger
* Juice and Grated Zest of Two Oranges
* Little Filtered Water

Put the duck breasts in an ovenproof dish and prick them all over. Rub the ginger and orange zest into the skin and pour over the orange juice and a little filtered water. Roast in a moderate oven until tender. Serve with roast potatoes and choice of vegetables of the day.

BAKED RAINBOW TROUT OR RED SNAPPER WITH GOOSEBERRY SAUCE (DAY FOUR)

* 1 Rainbow Trout or Red Snapper Per Person
* 1 Red Pepper (de-seeded and finely chopped)
* 4oz (100 grams) Hazelnuts (finely chopped - optional)
* 2-3 Tomatoes (blanched, skinned and chopped)
* Freshly Chopped Sorrel (to taste)

Clean the fish and rinse the cavity in salted water. Mix together all the ingredients for the stuffing and press lightly into the cavities. Brush with either hazelnut or palm oil, (if you're allergic to nuts you could perhaps use olive or grapeseed oil from day two and rotate as usual). Place in an ovenproof dish and bake in a moderate oven for fifteen to twenty minutes depending on the size of the fish. Serve with potatoes and your choice of vegetables from the day's list.

GOOSEBERRY SAUCE (DAY FOUR)

* 8oz (200 grams) Gooseberries
* Fructose (to taste)
* Tiny pinch Bicarbonate of Soda
* Filtered Water

Top and tail the gooseberries. Place in a heavy bottomed saucepan with the fructose and enough filtered water to cover the bottom of the pan. Bring to the boil and reduce the heat, add the bicarbonate of soda to neutralise some of the acid. Continue to simmer until the gooseberries are cooked and the liquid is well reduced. Serve with your choice from the day's list of meat and fish. Serves 4.

ROAST TURKEY WITH CRANBERRY OR GOOSEBERRY SAUCE (DAY FOUR)

* 1 Oven Ready Turkey (Free Range if possible)
* Hazelnut Oil for Basting (or grapeseed oil from day two, if allergic to nuts)
* 1 Lemon
* Sorrel (freshly chopped, to taste)
* Lemon Verbena (freshly chopped, to taste)

Rinse out the turkey cavity with salted water and place in a roasting tray. Prick the lemon all over, slice in half and place in the bird's cavity. Place in a moderate oven and cook for fifteen minutes a pound and fifteen minutes over, basting regularly) Serve with either homemade gooseberry or cranberry sauce. You could use ready made as long as you check the ingredients. Serve with roast or new potatoes and choice of vegetables from the day's list. Serves 6-8 people.

ROAST GOOSE WITH TOMATO AND AUBERGINE STUFFING (DAY FOUR)

- 1 Prepared Goose
- Hazelnut Oil (if allergic to nuts use Grapeseed Oil from day two and rotate as usual)

For the Stuffing

- 3 -4 Tomatoes (blanched, skinned and chopped)
- 1 Aubergine (diced)
- Freshly Chopped Lemon Verbena (to taste)
- Paprika Pepper (to taste)
- Mashed Potato (to bind)

Wash and dry the goose and prick the skin and place on a wire rack above the roasting tin so that the excess fat can drain away. Mix the ingredients for the stuffing and fill the bird's cavity. Brush with a little oil and place in a hot oven 220c gas mark 7 for the first fifteen to twenty minutes, then turn down to 160c gas mark 3. It's a good idea at this stage to turn the goose over onto its breast so that the excess fat can drain away. Cover it with foil and cook for a further two hours or so depending on its size. Remove the foil and turn the goose over again and return to the oven to brown. When cooked, garnish with sliced kiwi fruit and kumquats. Serve with roast or new potatoes and your choice of the day's vegetables and either gooseberry or cranberry sauce. Serves 4-6 people.

BRAISED HARE OR RABBIT CASSEROLE (DAY FOUR)

* 1 Large Rabbit or Hare (jointed)
* ½ - 1 Pint Well Flavoured Stock from Meat or Vegetables on Day Four's list
* 1 Aubergine (diced)
* 1 Red Pepper (de-seeded and diced)
* 1 Yellow or Green Pepper (de-seeded and diced)
* 4-5 Good Sized Potatoes
* 3-4 Tomatoes (blanched, skinned and chopped)
* Paprika or Cayenne (to taste)
* Hazelnut Oil or Goose Fat (or Grapeseed oil from day two if allergic to nuts and rotate as usual

Heat the oil in a wide bottomed pan and brown the rabbit joints on all sides to seal in the juices. Add the stock and the rest of the ingredients and cook in a pre heated moderate oven for around two hours or until the meat is tender. The gravy can be thickened by adding a dessertspoonful of potato flour to a little filtered water, mixing it to a paste and quickly stirring it in, keep on stirring as it thickens to avoid lumps. Serve with potatoes and your choice of vegetables from the day's list. Serves 4-6 people.

FISH PIE (DAY FOUR)

* 1½lb (600 grams) Haddock (steamed, skinned and boned)
* 2lb (800 grams) Cooked, Mashed Potatoes)
* 3-4 Tomatoes (blanched and skinned)
* Freshly Chopped Sorrel (to taste)
* Freshly Chopped Lemon Verbena (to taste)
* Paprika Pepper (to taste)

Flake the fish in an ovenproof dish. Add a layer of chopped tomatoes seasoned to taste with paprika. Sprinkle the chopped herbs over them and top with mashed potatoes. Bake in a moderate oven until golden brown and serve with choice of vegetables from day's list. Serves 4-6 people.

PAN-FRIED HADDOCK AND CHIPS (DAY FOUR)

* 1 Good Sized Haddock Fillet Per Person
* Potato Flour
* Hazelnut or Palm Oil or Grapeseed Oil (from Day Two)

Season the potato flour with paprika,, (if liked) and dip the fish fillets in it and fry in the oil of your choice until golden brown. Serve with chips cooked in the oil of your choice and serve with choice of vegetables from the day's list.

ROAST GROUSE (DAY FOUR)

* 1 Young Grouse Per Person
* Hazelnut Oil, Goose fat or Grapeseed Oil from Day Two (rotate as usual)

Heat the oil in a heavy bottomed pan and seal the birds quickly on all sides. Put them in a roasting dish, and cook in a pre-heated moderate oven, basting frequently until golden brown and tender. Serve with either gooseberry or cranberry sauce, roast potatoes and vegetables of your choice from the day's list.

ROAST DUCK WITH GOOSEBERRY SAUCE (DAY FOUR)

* 4-5lb Free Range Duck
* 6 fl oz Well Flavoured Stock
* Duck Giblets
* Potato Flour
* Goosefat, Hazelnut Oil (or Grapeseed Oil from Day Two)
* Grated Rind and Juice of an Orange (optional)
* Grated Root Ginger (to taste - optional)

Put the stock into a saucepan with the duck giblets, bring to the boil then reduce the heat and simmer for about an hour.

Rinse the bird and pat dry with unbleached kitchen paper. Place in a roasting dish and drizzle with the oil of your choice. If using, pour over the rind and juice of the orange and grated root ginger. Prick all over with a fork and cook in a pre-heated oven, 200c or gas mark 6 for twenty minutes a pound and twenty minutes over, basting occasionally. Turn up the heat to around 220c gas mark 7 for the last fifteen minutes before the duck is cooked to crisp up the skin. Strain the juices into a bowl and skim off the surface fat. Mix some potato flour (no more than a tablespoonful) with a little of the cooled and drained giblet stock, pour in the rest of the stock and add the meat juices. Re-heat stirring constantly until the gravy thickens. Serve with either gooseberry or cranberry sauce, boiled or roast potatoes and your choice of vegetables from the day's list. Serves 4-6 people.

SCALLOP STIR FRY (DAY FOUR)

* 1lb (400 grams) of Scallops (washed, bearded and sliced into 3-4 pieces)
* 1 Red Pepper (de-seeded and diced)
* 1 Green Pepper (de-seeded and diced)
* 1 Yellow Pepper (de-seeded and diced)
* 3-4 Tomatoes (blanched, skinned and chopped)
* 1lb of Cooked, Diced Potatoes
* 1 Aubergine (sliced)
* 1-2 Chillis or Pimentos (optional but de-seeded if using)
* Paprika or Cayenne Pepper (to taste)
* Palm or Hazelnut Oil (or an oil from day two if allergic to nuts and miss next normal rotation)

Heat the oil in a wok add all ingredients and stir fry over a fairly high heat until scallops have lost their opaqueness and the potatoes and aubergines are golden brown but the peppers are still crunchy. Serve with jacket potatoes or chips. Serves 4 people.

ROAST WOOD PIGEON (DAY FOUR)

* 1 Pigeon Per Person
* Hazelnut Oil (or Grapeseed Oil from Day Two)
* 2oz (50 grams) Chopped Hazelnuts (optional)
* 1½ Glasses Well Flavoured Turkey, Goose or Rabbit Stock

Pre-heat the oven to 190c gas mark 4-5, brush the prepared birds with the oil and place in a roasting tin. Pour in the stock and cook for around thirty minutes depending on size. You should increase the temperature to 200c gas mark 6 for the last few minutes to let them brown thoroughly. If using hazelnuts, scatter them over the birds breasts a few minutes before the end of the cooking time. Serve with gooseberry or cranberry sauce, potatoes and your choice of vegetables from the day's list.

BAKED PLANTAINS AND GREEN BANANAS

Plantains and green bananas are used as vegetables in many ethnic communities. To bake them just wrap them whole in tin foil and bake in a slow to moderate oven for around thirty minutes. Peel just before serving. They can also be served raw in salads, boiled, steamed, fried or microwaved whole for 3-4 minutes. As the skins are so tough, it's best to cut them into sections horizontally and peel each section before cooking.

DESSERTS FOR DAY FOUR

RHUBARB AND GINGER CRUMBLE

* 1lb (400 grams) Fresh Rhubarb (or frozen and defrosted)
* Grated Root Ginger or Powdered (to taste)
* Fructose (to taste)
* Pinch of Bicarbonate of Soda
* Filtered Water

For the Topping
* 4oz (100 grams) Buckwheat Flour
* 2oz (50 grams) Potato Flour
* 2oz (50 grams) Dessicated Coconut
* 4oz (100 grams) Tomor Margarine

Peel and chop the rhubarb. Put into a pan with enough filtered water to just cover the bottom. Bring to the boil and change the water, adding a small pinch of Bicarbonate of Soda. Bring to the boil again Remove from the heat and allow to cool. Meanwhile, mix the coconut and flours together and add the margarine, rub in until it resembles breadcrumbs. Put the rhubarb and ginger into an ovenproof dish and scatter the topping over it. Put into a pre-heated oven at 190c gas mark 4-5 bake for approximately twenty minutes or until golden brown. If you like and can tolerate nuts, try scattering a few chopped hazelnuts or brazils over the crumble five minutes before the end of the cooking time. Serve with potato flour custard, which I promise you is much nicer than it sounds. Serves 4 people.

POTATO FLOUR CUSTARD
(DAY FOUR)

* 1 Pint Coconut Milk
* 1 Rounded tablespoon Potato Flour
* Fructose (to taste)
* Vanilla Pod

The German occupation of the Channel Islands during World War Two, caused the islanders to suffer great hardships. Every type of commodity was in short supply and so people by necessity became very inventive, acorns were roasted and ground to make 'coffee', seawater was boiled to extract the salt and potatoes were made into flour, and used in a variety of ways. Potato flour custard, made with full cream Jersey milk was just one of them. I have adapted this wartime recipe and I hope you like it.

Mix the potato flour to a smooth paste with the fructose and a little of the coconut milk in a thick bottomed saucepan. Add the rest of the coconut milk and the vanilla pod, bring to the boil stirring constantly. Reduce the heat and simmer until the mixture thickens. Serves 4 people, with fruits of the day or rhubarb crumble etc. The vanilla pod can be re-used if you rinse it in filtered water, roll in fructose, then wrap in tin foil or greaseproof paper and store in the fridge.

BUCKWHEAT PANCAKES (DAY FOUR)

* 4oz (100 grams) Buckwheat Flour
* 1 Duck Egg
* ½ Pint Coconut Milk
* Little Filtered Water if necessary
* Hazelnut or Palm Oil for frying.

Combine the buckwheat and egg in a mixing bowl, gradually beat in the coconut milk and water. Fry the pancakes in the usual way and serve with stewed fruits of the day. Make 3-4 small pancakes.

FRESH FRUIT SALAD (DAY FOUR)

* 3 Oranges (peeled and sliced horizontally)
* 3 Kiwi Fruits (peeled and sliced)
* 3 Bananas (peeled and sliced)
* 2 Pawpaws (peeled and sliced)
* 3 Sharron Fruits (if in season - peeled and sliced)
* Pure Orange Juice
* ½lb (200 grams) Fresh Pitted Dates
* Slivers of Fresh Coconut

Combine all the fruits with the juice and serve. Serves 4 people.

SNACKS/OCCASIONAL TREATS (DAY FOUR)

BASIC CAKE MIXTURE

* 6oz (150 grams) Buckwheat Flour
* 2oz (50 grams) Potato Flour
* 8oz (200 grams) Tomor Margarine
* 4 Duck Eggs
* 6oz Fructose (or to taste)
* 1 Rounded Teaspoon Cream of Tartar
* 1 Level Teaspoon Bicarbonate of Soda

Sift the flours with the raising agents. Cream the margarine and fructose until light and fluffy, and add the eggs and filtered water before folding in the flour. Mix well and divide between 2 x 8" greased cake tins. If the mixture is too dry add a little coconut milk to obtain the right consistency, but don't make it too soft or the finished cakes will turn out soggy in the middle. Bake in a slow to moderate oven until golden brown and firm to the touch.

GINGER CAKE

Add two teaspoons of powdered ginger to the above mixture and bake as above. For a steamed ginger pudding, use a greased pyrex type pudding basin and fill two thirds full to allow the mixture to rise. Cover with oiled greaseproof paper and steam for about an hour and a half until well risen and spongy to the touch. Serve with potato flour 'custard'.

CURRANT CAKE

Add 4oz scalded currants to the basic cake mix and bake as normal. For a change you could do a steamed currant pudding using same method as ginger pudding. Or stewed fruits of the day covered with half the basic cake mix and steamed in usual way and served with potato flour 'custard'.

CHOICE OF FRUITS AND NUTS OF THE DAY (DAY FOUR)

CHAPTER EIGHT

NON ROTATING RECIPES

In this section of the book I am including some recipes donated by friends and food companies who specialise in products suitable for allergy sufferers and you may find them helpful if you're not following the rotation diet rigidly.

The following two recipes are reproduced by kind permission of Osgrow Ltd, Tybroughton Hall, Whitchurch, Shropshire SY13 3BB. Tel 01948 780654 Fax 01948 780664. Contact them at the above address for a list of regional distributors who will deliver meat to your door.

CHESTNUT AND OSTRICH SOUP

* 1.5 Litres Good Ostrich Stock incorporating OSGROW Diced Ostrich Steak
* 450 grams Chestnuts or 350 grams Unsweetened Chestnut Puree
* 35 grams Fat or Oil of your choice
* 1 Carrot (sliced)
* 1 Onion (Sliced)
* 1 Celery Stick (sliced)
* 1 Medium Potato (sliced)
* 1 Bayleaf (cracked)
* 1 Sprig of Thyme
* 1 Clove of Garlic
* Croutons of Fried Bread
* Chopped Parsley
* Sea Salt and Freshly Ground Black Pepper

Melt the fat in a pan and add the carrots, onion, celery and potato. Saute gently until lightly coloured. Add the peeled chestnuts or puree and the diced ostrich steak cover with stock and add the bayleaf and sprig of thyme. Simmer for about forty minutes or until the vegetables and chestnuts are tender. Remove the bayleaf and thyme and any bones. Puree the vegetables and sieve. Season to taste. Crush the clove of garlic with a little sea salt and mix with some oil of your choice. Toss the croutons in a frying pan with the oil and garlic until golden brown. Add some chopped parsley and serve.

OSTRICH STEAKS IN ORANGE GLAZE WITH KIWI FRUIT

* 400 grams Osgrow Ostrich Fillet Steaks
* 1 Large Onion
* 2 Kiwi Fruit
* 2 Teasponnful Oil of your choice
* 1 Tablespoonful Clear Honey
* Strips of Orange Zest - Juice of Half an Orange
* Watercress to garnish

Grate the zest from half of the orange. Cut the orange in two along the grated half and reserve the juice and zest. Separately cut the second half into four crescents and reserve. Peel the kiwi fruit and cut them into four slices. Place some oil in a pan and fry the ostrich steaks for approximately three minutes to medium rare, brown on both sides. Remove from the heat and place the steaks on to a warm plate and keep warm. Grate the onion into the frying pan and brown lightly. Add the honey and stir in when it darkens slightly and the reserved juice and zest and stir until syrupy. Add the ostrich to the pan with the orange wedges and kiwi fruit. Toss them in the glaze and when coated arrange on a warm serving dish. Pour the remaining glaze over the meat. Garnish with watercress and serve.

The following recipes were donated by Cauldron Foods Ltd. Unites 1-2 Portishead Business Park, Portishead, Bristol, BS20 9BF and are reproduced with their kind permission. For a comprehensive recipe leaflet write to them at the above address.

NUTTY TOFU BURGERS

* 1 Packet Cauldron Foods Original Tofu (mashed)
* 3 Tablespoons Soy Sauce (check label for additives)
* 1 Carrot (coarsely grated)

* 1 Garlic Clove (crushed)
* 2 slices Wholemeal Bread (crumbed)
* 2 Tablespoons Chopped Nuts of your choice
* 1 Spring Onion (finely chopped)
* 1 Tablespoon Tomato Puree
* 1 Size 3 Free Range Egg
* 1 Tablespoon Fresh Coriander (chopped)
* Sea Salt and Freshly Ground Black Pepper (to taste)
* Your choice of oil for frying

Mix the tofu and soy sauce in a bowl and leave for ten minutes, then squeeze out any excess moisture. Mix all the ingredients except the oil in a bowl. Form into four burgers, chill for twenty minutes. Lightly brush the burgers with oil and cook under a medium grill for fifteen minutes, turning frequently. Alternatively, grill on a barbecue.

TOFU AND VEGETABLE LASAGNE

* 1 Packet of Cauldron Foods Original Tofu (diced)
* 2 Courgettes (halved lengthways and sliced)
* 1 Red Pepper (de-seeded and diced)
* 1 Green Pepper (de-seeded and diced)
* 1 Large Onion (diced)
* 7oz (200 grams) Tomatoes (blanched, skinned and diced)
* 1 Clove Garlic (crushed)
* 4 Tablespoons Olive Oil
* 2oz (50 grams) Pitted Black Olives (halved)
* 2oz (50 grams) Butter
* 2oz (50 grams) Flour (of your choice)
* 1½ pints (900mls) Milk
* 3 Bayleaves
* 5oz (150 grams) Grated Mozzarella Cheese
* 9 Lasagne Sheets (the type which doesn't require pre-cooking)
* Sea Salt and Freshly Ground Pepper (to taste)

Pre-heat the oven to 230c/450f/Gas Mark 8. Place the prepared tofu, courgettes, peppers, onion, tomatoes, garlic and olive oil in a roasting tin. Season, add two bayleaves torn in half, mix to coat the vegetables in oil. Place in the oven on a high shelf and cook for forty minutes. Meanwhile make the sauce. Place the butter in a saucepan with the flour and melt over a gentle heat, stirring constantly until the mixture forms a roux and leaves the sides of the pan. Gradually add the milk in stages stirring continually to avoid lumps forming. Once all the milk is in, add the bayleaf and season to taste. Continue cooking for 1-2 minutes until thickened, remove from the heat. Once the vegetables are cooked remove them from the oven and reduce the heat to 180c/350f/Gas Mark 4. Mix the olives into the vegetables. To assemble the lasagne, place a quarter of the sauce in the bottom of an oblong dish, (approx 17cm x 26cm/7" by 10") cover with a third of the cooked vegetables, a quarter of the mozzarella and finally, three sheets of lasagne. Repeat this process twice, top the final layer of lasagne sheets with sauce and mozzarella cheese. Place in the oven for 40-45 minutes. Serves four people with a green salad.

HONEY AND MUSTARD GLAZED ROOT VEGETABLES

* 1 Packet Cauldron Original Tofu (diced)
* 2 Tablespoons Wholegrain Mustard
* 2 Tablespoons Honey
* 1/4 Teaspoon Sea Salt
* Freshly ground Black Pepper
* 3 Tablespoonful Olive Oil
* 1 Medium Parsnip (diced)
* 1 Large Carrot (diced)
* 1 Onion (diced) or 4 Shallots (halved)
* 1 Potato (diced)

Pre-heat the oven to 200c 400f/Gas Mark 6. Mix the mustard, honey, salt pepper and oil together in a large bowl. Add the tofu and vegetables to the bowl, mix well to coat in the glaze. Transfer to a roasting tin, place on the top shelf of the oven and cook for thirty five minutes. Serves two with crusty bread. Preparation time fifteen minutes.

MEXICAN TOFU AND BEAN SOUP

* 1 Packet Cauldron Foods Original Tofu (diced)
* 3 Tablespoons Vegetable Oil
* 1 Medium Onion (diced)
* 1 Garlic Clove (crushed)
* 1 Green Pepper (halved)
* 1 Teaspoon Hot Chilli Powder
* 1 Teaspoon Paprika
* 1 Vegetarian Stock Cube (dissolved in a pint/600ml boiling filtered water)
* 3 Tablespoons Tomato Puree
* 14oz (400 grams) Tin of Chopped Tomatoes
* 8oz (225 grams) Tin Red Kidney Beans (drained)
* 3oz (75 grams) Sweetcorn (frozen)
* 2 Tablespoons Fresh Coriander (roughly chopped)
* 1 Teaspoon Cornflour dissolved in 5 Tablespoons Filtered Water

Gently heat the oil in a pan, add the onion, and cook for five minutes. Meanwhile, pre-heat a grill, place the peppers under it, skin side up until black and blisted. Remove, peel off the skin, cut into dice. Add the garlic, peppers, chilli and paprika to the onions and fry for one minute. Add the puree, dissolved stock, tomatoes, kidney beans, tofu and sweetcorn. Bring to the boil and simmer for twenty minutes uncovered. Pour the dissolved cornflour into the soup along with the coriander and stir until thickened.

RASPBERRY AND TOFU BRULEE

* 1 Packet Cauldron Foods Original Tofu
* 2 Tablespoons Clear Honey or Golden Syrup
* 7oz (200 grams) Fresh or Frozen and Defrosted Raspberries
* 4 Dessertspoons Soft Brown Sugar
* Spring of Fresh Mint

Place the tofu, honey and raspberries in a food processor or liquidiser, blend until smooth. Divide the mixture between the ramekin dishes. Sprinkle a spoonful of sugar over each ramekin. Place the ramekins under a pre-heated grill until the sugar melts and caramelises. Remove, cool and refrigerate for about an hour before serving. Decorate the tops with mint leaves.

DARK CHOCOLATE PIE WITH PASSION FRUIT SAUCE

* 1 Packet Cauldron Foods Original Tofu
* 9oz (250 grams) Digestive Biscuits
* 5oz (150 grams) Butter (or Soya Margarine)
* 2 Lemons
* 2 Oranges
* 4 Passion Fruit
* 2 Tablespoons Castor Sugar
* 2 Teaspoons Cornflour dissolved in 6 Teaspoons Filtered Water
* ½ Pint (300ml) Filtered Water
* 1 Level Teaspoon Gelozone (vegetarian gelatine)
* 1 Tablespoon Golden Syrup
* 7oz (200 grams) Plain Chocolate*

* Check small print as the chocolate may contain traces of nuts. So be wary if they are a problem to you.

Line a 8" spring clip or loose bottomed flan tin with greaseproof paper and oil lightly. Prepare the base by putting the biscuits in a sealed plastic bag and crushing them with a rolling pin until fine. Place the butter in a pan over gentle heat until melted. Remove from the heat, add the crushed biscuits, mix together well. Line the base and sides of the tin with the mixture pressing down gently with the back of a spoon. Place in the fridge for one hour to harden. Prepare the sauce by placing the juice of the oranges, lemons and the insides of the passionfruit in a saucepan along with the sugar. Add the dissolved cornflour to the pan, mix and heat gently until thickened. Pass the sauce through a sieve to remove the pips and pith, allow to cool. Break up the chocolate, place in a glass bowl. Place boiling water into a larger bowl and sit the bowl of chocolate in it until it is completely melted. Place the filtered water into a saucepan, sprinkle in the gelozone, mix. Place over a low heat and bring to a gentle simmer for two minutes. Place the tofu, syrup, melted chocolate and dissolved Gelozone into a food processor/blender and blend until smooth. Pour the mixture into the prepared biscuit base. Place in the fridge for two hours to set. Once set it can be frozen for up to one month in the tin. The sauce can also be frozen. Serve slices on a plate with the sauce pour over the top.

The following recipes are reproduced with the kind permission of Clearspring Ltd. 19A Acton Park Estate, London W3 7QE. Tel++44 (0) 180 749 1781 Fax ++44 (0) 181 746 2259

For a comprehensive range of recipes and lists of their products contact the company at the above address.

All the Clearspring products featured in these recipes are easily available at most healthfood stores.

BREAKFAST IDEAS WITH RICE DREAM
CREAMY HEARTY OATMEAL

* 2 Cups Original Rice Dream
* 1 Cup Rolled Oats
* 1/4 Cup Raisins or Chopped Dates
* Pinch Sea Salt
* 1/4 Teaspoon Cinnamon (optional)
* Sprinkle Roasted Nuts or Seeds

Place all ingredients in a saucepan. Bring to the boil. Cover (leaving lid ajar to prevent boiling over). Reduce heat to very low and simmer for ten minutes. Stir often. Serve topped with roasted nuts or seeds and fresh fruits of your choice.

GROUND RICE PUDDING

* 3oz (75 grams) Ground Rice
* Maple Syrup or Date Sugar (to taste)
* 1 Litre Rice Milk
* 1 Block Creamed Coconut (optional)
* 1 Vanilla Pod

Put all the ingredients into a heavy bottomed saucepan and bring to the boil stirring constantly. Reduce the heat and simmer, still stirring, until the pudding thickens. Remove the vanilla pod. Rinse it in filtered water before rolling in sugar or fructose. Wrap it in tin foil and store in the fridge until needed again. The pudding serves four people.

PANCAKES

* 1 Cup of Flour (of your choice)
* 1 Cup Original Rice Dream
* 2 Tablespoons Oil (your choice)
* 1 Teaspoon Egg Replacer Powder
* 1½ Teaspoon Baking Powder
* 1/4 Teaspoon Sea Salt

Gently mix all ingredients and let batter stand for 2 minutes. Mix in two more tablespoons of Rice Dream. Lightly oil a pan or griddle, heat over medium-high heat. Use a 1/4 cup of batter for each pancake. Cook about 1½ minutes each side. Serve with your favourite toppings.

BANANA-BERRY SMOOTHIE

* 1 Ripe Banana (skin removed and frozen)
* 2 Cups Original or Vanilla Rice Dream
* 2 Tablespoons Blueberry Conserve
* Optional Fresh Berries (of your choice)

Cut banana into chunks and place in a blender with conserve, berries and Rice Dream. Blend until creamy and smooth. Makes 2 generous servings.

SAVOURY SOUPS

VEGETABLE CHOWDER

* 1 Tablespoon Oil (your choice)
* 1 Small Onion (diced)
* 1 Large Celery Stalk (thinly sliced)
* 1 Large Carrot (thinly sliced)
* 1 Clove Garlic (crushed)
* 2 Cups Filtered Water
* 1 Medium Sized Potato (peeled and diced)
* 2 Ripe Tomatoes (blanched, skinned and chopped)
* ½ Cup Fresh or Frozen Corn
* 2 Tablespoons Tamari Soy Sauce
* 1 Teaspoon Basil (chopped)
* 1 Large Bayleaf
* ½ Teaspoon Sea Salt
* Freshly Ground Black Pepper
* 2 Cups Original Rice Dream

In a 3 quart saucepan, saute the onions in oil until translucent. Add celery, carrots and garlic, saute for several more minutes. Add water, potatoes, corn and seasonings, bring to the boil, reduce heat and simmer. Cover and cook for 15 minutes. Add tomatoes and simmer for 15 minutes longer. Add Rice Dream and adjust seasonings to taste. Serves 5-6 people.

CREAM OF BROCCOLI AND YELLOW SQUASH SOUP

* 4 Tablespoons Oil (your choice)
* 1 Medium Onion (diced)
* 1 Large Bayleaf
* 2 Medium Garlic Cloves (crushed)
* 3 Cups Broccoli (chopped)
* 2 Cups Yellow Crook necked Squash, (sliced - or another variety if unavailable)
* 1 Teaspoon Sea Salt
* 2½ Cups Filtered Water or Vegetable Stock
* 2 Cups Original Rice Dream

* ½ Teaspoon each of Basil, Thyme and Marjoram
* 1 Cup Broccoli Florets
* Freshly Ground Black Pepper to taste
* Fresh Chives (finely chopped - optional)

Saute onions and garlic in a 3 quart saucepan over medium heat until onions are translucent. Add chopped broccoli, squash, bay leaf, salt and water/stock. Cover and cook for 15 minutes (or until the broccoli is tender). Using a food processor or blender, puree the mixture until smooth and creamy. Return puree to pot, whisk in Rice Dream and all seasonings and simmer over low heat for 10 minutes. Steam broccoli florets 3-5 minutes, add to the soup. Gently stir and serve immediately topped with chopped chives. Serves 6-8 people.

RICE DREAM (BECHAMEL) CREAM SAUCE

* 4 Tablespoons Butter, Ghee or Olive Oil
* 1 Small Onion (finely chopped)
* 1 Clove Garlic (minced)
* 6 Tablespoons Whole Wheat or Brown Rice Flour
* Optional Splash White Wine or Lemon Juice
* 1 Cup Original Rice Dream
* ½ Cup Filtered Water/Vegetable Stock
* Pinch of Dried Dill
* ½ Teaspoon Sea Salt
* Freshly Ground Black Pepper (to taste)

Saute onions and garlic in a heavy saucepan in the butter/oil until soft and translucent. Sprinkle in flour and stir frequently for 5 minutes. Slowly add Rice Dream, water/stock and seasonings. Whisk until well blended. Increase heat and allow the mixture to come briefly to a boil. Reduce heat to low and simmer for 5 minutes, stirring often. Taste, adjust seasonings and/or sauce thickness by adding more water or flour in small amounts. Serve immediately or allow to cool and refrigerate for later use. Yield 2 cups.

FETTUCINI PRIMAVERA WITH BECHAMEL SAUCE

* 3 Tablespoons Extra Virgin Olive Oil
* 2 Cloves Garlic (minced)
* 1 Head Broccoli (thinly cut)
* 1 Large Red Pepper (thinly sliced)
* 10 Large Mushrooms (thinly sliced)
* 1 Small Red Onion (diced finely)
* 1 Cup Frozen Baby Peas (thawed)
* ½ Cup Fresh Basil (cut into strips)
* ½ Cup Black Olives (sliced)
* 12 oz Fettucini Pasta
* 3 Cups Bechamel Sauce (see previous recipe)
* Garnish - Basil Flowers or Leaves (optional)

In a medium pan, saute broccoli and garlic in the olive oil for 5 minutes. Add peppers and mushrooms, saute over medium heat for 5-10 minutes more depending upon how well cooked you prefer your vegetables. Stir in the peas; cook a few more minutes until the mixture is hot. Add olives and basil; cover and set aside. Cook pasta following package instructions. Serve topped with sauteed vegetables and a generous portion of Bechamel Sauce. Garnish with basil flowers or leaves. Serves 4-6 people.

CREAM OF CAULIFLOWER SOUP

* 1 Teaspoon Unrefined Sesame or Sunflower Oil
* 1 Medium Onion (diced)
* 2 Bayleaves
* Pinch Sea Salt
* 3 Cups Filtered Water
* 1 x 5" of Kombu Sea Vegetable
* 1 Medium Cauliflower (cut into florets)
* 1 Cup Soya Milk (optional)
* 3 Tablespoons (or to taste) Clearspring Organic White Miso Or 1-2 Teaspoons (or to taste) Organic Mugi or Gemmai Miso
* Chopped Parsley and Bread Croutons to Garnish

Heat the oil in a saucepan and add the onions and bayleaves and saute for 5-7 minutes with the sea salt. Add the water and kombu and bring to the boil. Add the cauliflower and cook over a medium heat for 15-20 minutes. Add the soya milk (optional) and miso and gently simmer for 2-3 minutes. Remove the kombu and keep to re-use in your bean dishes. Blend the soup until smooth and creamy and serve hot or chilled with the garnishes. Serves 4. This recipe can also be used as a wonderful gluten and dairy free alternative to bechamel sauce.

GRAIN AND VEGETABLE STEW

* 3 Cups Filtered Water
* 1 Leek (cut thinly)
* 2 Carrots (cut into thin matchsticks)
* 1 Cup Small Cauliflower Florets
* 3 Cups of Cooked Left Over Grain (your choice)
* 1½ Tablespoons (or to taste) Clearspring Mugi or Gemmai Miso
* 2 Tablespoons Juice Squeezed from Freshly Grated Ginger Root
* Garnishes: Roasted Seeds, Chopped Salad Onions, Toasted Strips of Nori Sea Vegetable

Bring the water to the boil. Add the leeks and cook uncovered for 2-3 minutes. Add the rest of the vegetables and cooked grain and simmer for 10-15 minutes (vegetables are cooked) using a flame diffuser to prevent scorching on the bottom of the pan. Add the seasonings and miso and gently simmer for 3-4 minutes. Serve with choice of garnishes.

Miso is a very versatile seasoning and can be used to flavour soups, stews and bean dishes. To gain the full benefit of miso's enzymatic properties, add at the end of the cooking time and just simmer over a very low flame for 1-2 minutes. Miso is also wonderful for dips, gravies, spreads and pickles. It makes a delicious dressing for salads, noodles, grains and beans, tofu, vegetable protein and grilled dishes.

VEGETARIAN MISO SOUP

* 50 grams Wakame, (soaked in filtered water 3-4 minutes and sliced into small pieces)
* 3 Cups Filtered Water
* 1 Small Onion or Leek (finely cut)
* 1 Cup of Carrot or Pumpkin (diced)
* 1½ Teaspoon Clearspring Traditional Miso
* Garnish: Finely Chopped Salad Onions and Bread Croutons

Bring the water to the boil, add the onion or leek and cook uncovered for 2 minutes. Add the carrot or pumpkin and Wakame, and simmer for 10 minutes. Puree the Miso with a little soup liquid in a bowl, reduce the heat to a minimum, add diluted miso and simmer for 2 minutes more. Serve with the garnishes.

VEGETARIAN PAELLA WITH ARAME

* 2 Tablespoons Unrefined Oil (of your choice)
* 1 Leek or Onion (finely chopped)
* 1 Cup Mushrooms (quartered and sprinkled with a few drops of lemon juice)
* Clearspring Shoyu Soya Sauce to season
* 2 Carrots (sliced into thin rounds)
* 1 Teaspoon Turmeric (optional - to colour the rice yellow)
* 2½ Cups cooked Brown Rice
* ½ Cup Arame washed in Cold Filtered Water
* ½ Cup Cooked Peas
* Garnish Lemon Slices and Freshly Chopped Parsley

Heat a large frying pan and add the oil, leeks or onions, mushrooms, a few drops of Shoyu and saute for 2-3 minutes. Add the carrots and cook for 7-10 minutes with ½ cup filtered water and the turmeric (optional) Add the cooked rice and washed Arame and mix thoroughly but gently with the sauteed vegetables. Transfer to a serving dish and garnish with the cooked peas, lemon and parsley.

SEA PALM WITH PRAWNS OR ROASTED ALMONDS

* 1 Cup of Sea Palm, (rinsed and soaked for 10 minutes in filtered water)
* 1 Tablespoon Oil of your choice
* 1 Clove Fresh Garlic or Onions (chopped very fine)
* 1 Tablespoon Clearspring Shoyu Soya Sauce
* Apple Juice Concentrate or Mirin
* 1 Cup Peeled Cooked Prawns or Roasted Almonds
* 1 Cup Sweetcorn Kernels
* Garnish - Chopped Parsley or Fresh Coriander Leaves

Cook the sea palm in its own soaking water (if not too salty) for 20 minutes or until the water has evaporated. Heat a light pan (wok or stainless steel saucepan) add the oil and garlic and saute over a medium flame until the garlic is golden. Add the cooked Sea Palm and season with the Shoyu and sweetener to taste. Add the prawns (or roasted almonds) and sweetcorn and mix thoroughly but gently. Serve hot with the garnish.

DESSERTS WITH AMAZAKE

Amazake is a traditional sweetener which is used as a base for delicious wholefood desserts and drinks. It is made by cooking cereal grains with rice koji (rice which has been inoculated with a special culture). The enzymes in the koji break down the starches in the grains into their natural sugars to produce a rich creamy pudding which is nutritious and easily digestible. If you have never tasted amazake, you will be amazed by its natural sweetness.

Due to its mild composition, colour and full creamy taste, amazake lends itself to being included in desserts, drinks, cakes, confectionery and ice cream. It can also be used directly as a spread for rusks, toast, bread, rice, cakes, pancakes etc. The creamy taste makes amazake particularly useful for people with milk allergy.

Amazake can be made from any type of grain, thereby providing a great variety of flavours and consistencies. At present, rice, oat and millet amazake are available from the Clearspring Company who sell through many health food shops throughout the country. Here are just a few of their recipes reproduced with their kind permission:-

COFFEE PUDDING

* 300 grams Rice Amazake
* 350ml Filtered Water
* 1-2 Tablespoons Yannoh Instant (or other coffee substitute)
* 2 Tablespoons Kuzu, Arrowroot or Cornflour
* Pinch of Sea Salt

Mix the contents of one jar of rice amazake and 300ml filtered water in a saucepan and bring to the boil while stirring, adding a pinch of sea salt. Meanwhile dissolve the coffee substitute in some filtered water and add to the mixture. Taste and add more coffee substitute if required. Sieve if smoother texture is desired. Dissolve thickener in a few tablespoons of filtered water and add to the boiling amazake while stirring. Allow to boil for a minute or so until sufficiently thickened. Serve in a dessert bowl and decorate with a strawberry, slice of kiwi, orange segment or almond sauce.

CHOCOLATE PUDDING

Follow the recipe for coffee pudding but substitute 1-2 tablespoons cocoa for the coffee and serve in the same way.

LEMON PUDDING

Follow the recipe for coffee pudding but replace coffee with juice and grated rind of one lemon.

ORANGE PUDDING

Follow the recipe for coffee pudding but replace coffee with the juice and grated rind of one orange.

VANILLA PUDDING

* 350 grams Millet Amazake
* 350 ml Vanilla Soya Milk (or Banana or Apricot flavoured)
* 2 Tablespoons Kuzu, Arrowroot or Cornflour
* Pinch of Sea Salt

Follow the same preparation method as that used for the coffee pudding. It's delicious served with coffee sauce.

HAZELNUT CUSTARD

* 370 grams Amazake (Rice or Millet)
* 350 ml Filtered Water
* 75 grams Hazelnuts
* 2 Tablespoons Kuzu, Arrowroot or Cornflour
* Pinch of Sea Salt

Roast the hazelnuts and grind until fine in a blender. Add the contents of one jar of rice or millet amazake, 300ml filtered water and the salt in a saucepan. Bring to the boil while stirring. Dissolve the thickener in 50ml of water and add while stirring. Continue to boil until it is sufficiently thickened. Serve with a few hazelnuts as decoration.

ALMOND SAUCE

* 50 grams White Almond Puree
* 50 grams Amazake (variety of your choice)
* 1 Tablespoon Rice Syrup
* 50 ml Warm Filtered Water
* Pinch of Sea Salt

Mix all above ingredients in a mortar or blender to a smooth sauce and serve on puddings, ice cream or cake.

COFFEE SAUCE

Recipe as for almond sauce but include 1-2 tablespoons coffee substitute. Blend and serve on puddings, ice cream or cake.

CHOCOLATE DRINK

* 300 grams Rice Amazake
* 350 ml Filtered Water
* 1 Tablespoon Cocoa Powder
* Pinch Sea Salt

Mix amazake, water and salt in a saucepan and bring to the boil while stirring. Dissolve the cocoa powder in some cold water and add. Allow to boil for a while and sieve to remove husks. Tastes delicious served warm or cold.

AMAZAKE GINGER DRINK

* 300 grams Rice Amazake
* 350 ml Filtered Water
* 2 Teaspoons Ginger Juice (from grated root ginger)
* Pinch Sea Salt

Mix amazake, water and salt in a saucepan and bring to the boil stirring constantly. Pour the drink through a sieve to remove the husks. Add the ginger juice to the hot drink. In winter it is a delicious warming drink or dessert. In summer it can be cooled in the fridge and served cold. It then tastes deliciously refreshing and invigorating.

LEMON MOUSSE (DAIRY FREE)

* 3 Cups Filtered Water
* Pinch of Sea Salt
* 3-4 Tablespoons Clearspring Agar Flakes
* Cereal Malt Sweetener (to taste)
* ½ Cup Apple Juice Concentrate
* 1 Tablespoon Grated Lemon Rind
* Few Drops Pure Vanilla Extract (optional)
* 2 Tablespoons Tahini Sesame Spread

Bring the water to the boil and add the rest of the ingredients, except the tahini. Simmer for 10 minutes until the agar flakes are completely dissolved. Carefully dilute the tahini with some of the hot liquid then stir in with the rest. Pour the mixture into a glass or ceramic bowl and leave to set for 1-2 hours. Blend into a creamy consistency, adding some water or fresh apple juice if it is too thick.

BAKED STUFFED APPLES

* 4 Large Apples
* ½ Cup Sultanas
* 1-3 teaspoon Clearspring Organic Mugi Miso or ½ Teaspoon White Miso
* 1 Teaspoon Grated Orange or Lemon Rind
* 1½ Tablespoons Tahini
* 1/4 Teaspoon Cinnamon or Nutmeg Powder
* 2 Tablespoons Corn and Barley Malt

Pre-heat your oven to medium. Core the apples. Mix all the other ingredients very well then pack the mixture to very firmly fill the hole in the centre of each apple. Place the apples on a baking tray with a little filtered water underneath. Cover with aluminium foil (optional) and cook until done, approximately 20-30 minutes. Serve hot or chilled.

BLUEBERRY MUFFINS

* 3/4 Cup Wholemeal Flour
* 3/4 Cup Unbleached White Flour
* ½ Cup Corn Meal
  (or 2 cups in total of the flour of your choice)
* 1 Tablespoon Baking Powder
* 1/4 Teaspoon Sea Salt
* 6 Tablespoons Oil (your choice)
* 2 or Regular Tofu or 1 Beaten Egg
* 1 Cup Original Rice Dream
* 1/3 Cup Maple Syrup
* 1 Cup Fresh or Frozen Blueberries

Pre-heat the oven to 375F. Sift or mix all dry ingredients. In a separate bowl, mix all wet ingredients. If using tofu, puree in a blender with Rice Dream, then add to other wet ingredients. Stir wet ingredients into dry ingredients, just enough to mix. Oil muffin tin or line with bun cases. Spoon in the batter, filling the cups 2/3 full. Bake for 20-25 minutes, until golden brown. Makes 1 dozen.

As I mentioned earlier all the recipes in this section were reproduced with the kind permission of the Clearspring Company Ltd and for a comprehensive list of their recipes and products you can write to them at the address given earlier.

The following five recipes were donated by a Portuguese friend of mine called Ji, without whose enthusiasm and encouragement I would never have finished this book.

SQUIDS PAQUITO

Clean the squids not forgetting to remove the inner bone or beak. Cut them into rings. Fry one onion, finely diced, in butter with crushed garlic and one or two bayleaves. Add the squid rings and cook for one or two minutes. Add tomatoes, (without skin or seeds) or tomato pulp and a little stock or water and cook until the squids are tender.

Make one large cup of white sauce and add to the stew. Before serving add 1/4 cup of cream, top with chopped parsley. Serve with boiled rice.

COD FISH WITH CREAM

Place a layer of flaked, skinned and boned, cod fish into an ovenproof dish, lightly mash it with your hand to check for bones. Top with one layer of boiled potatoes, another layer of bechamel type sauce and so on, to finish top with a layer of hard boiled eggs cut into rings, pour over a generous amount of cream sprinkle with cheese and heat through until the cheese is melted. Sprinkle with herbs of your choice and serve.

BAKED SWORDFISH

For each slice of fish take one square of foil. Place fish in the middle of the foil square. Top with onion rings. Season with salt, pepper and paprika. Sprinkle with dry white wine if tolerated (fish stock if not) Close foil making a small parcel. Place the parcels in an ovenproof dish. Bake until just cooked. Serve with new potatoes and salad.

Alternative: Try Lime juice and coriander as an alternative to wine and onions.

OCTOPUS SALAD

Clean small octopus and freeze. Freezing breaks the fibres and makes the fish more tender. Boil the fish, cooking until tender. Soak small butter beans overnight and boil. Cut octopus into small bits. In a bowL, mix the beans, octopus, finely chopped raw onions, finely chopped garlic, (optional) and parsley. Season with olive oil and a little wine vinegar serve cold with black olives. This is also a good way of serving canned tuna fish.

FRIED SQUIDS

Clean the squids and cut them into rings. Make a fine batter in the usual way, (using flour and milk of your choice) dip squid rings in batter and fry them in hot oil. Serve on a bed of rice with lemon rings and a Mediterranean salad.

HADDOCK AND DILL FISH CAKES

A good sized haddock fillet, poached in filtered water then skinned and carefully boned. Flake it into a bowl with a few finely chopped sprigs of fresh dill (to taste) add celery and fennel seeds to taste and mashed potatoes. The best mix seems to be 50-50 fish and potatoes but you can add more or less if you choose. Form into flat cakes. If you wish, you can brush them with soya milk then dip them into soya or potato flour, personally, I prefer them plain, just fried in a choice of oil of the day. Serve garnished with chopped herbs and choice of vegetables.

SALMON AND PARSLEY FISH CAKES

As above but use a fillet of salmon, a handful of chopped chives and a few springs of fresh parsley to taste.

SCALLOP STIR FRY WITH DILL SAUCE

* 1lb (400 grams) Scallops (washed and sliced in half)
* 1 Bulb of Fennel (washed and sliced horizontally)
* 1 Red Pepper (de-seeded and cut into strips)
* 1 Green or Yellow Pepper (de-seeded and cut into strips)
* 1/4 pint of well flavoured fish stock
* 4 Sticks Celery (washed and chopped)
* 3 Carrots (cut into Julienne Strips)
* ½lb (200 grams) Green Beans (sliced)
* ½lb (200 grams) Kidney Beans (cooked)

For the Oil and Herb Marinade

* Handful Chopped Dill
* Few Lovage Leaves (chopped)
* Celery Seeds (to taste)
* Fennel Seeds (to taste)
* Hazelnut Oil (or Grapeseed Oil from Day Two)

First wash the scallops really well. Remove the beards and black part and cut them into three or four pieces, depending on size. Marinade the scallops in the oil and herb dressing for at least two hours. Transfer to a heavy bottomed frying pan or wok and cook in your choice of oil, over high heat until the scallops begin to lose their opaqueness (they cook extremely quickly). Lift out and keep warm. Add a tiny bit more oil if necessary and add the vegetables to the pan. Cook for very few minutes so they remain crunchy, lift out and keep warm. Add the fish stock to the juices in the pan and stir well. Thicken with a little potato flour slaked in fish stock and add more chopped dill bring to the boil stirring constantly until the sauce thickens, serve with the rest of the ingredients and wild rice, if liked and tolerated. Serves 4-6 people.

CELERY AND FENNEL SOUP

* 1½ -2 Pints Good Stock (this can be either Poultry, Rabbit Fish or Vegetable so long as it has a good flavour)
* ½ Head of Celery
* Few Carrots
* 2-3 Potatoes
* 1 Bulb of Fennel
* 4oz Kidney Beans (soaked overnight)
* Celery Seeds (to taste)
* Fennel Seeds (to taste)
* Ground Cardamon (to taste)
* 2oz Wild Rice

Dice all the vegetables and add to the stock with the rest of the ingredients. Bring to the boil, then reduce the heat and simmer until ready. You can either blend half and return it to the pan to reheat and serve or if you prefer, you can blend the whole lot for a smoother soup and serve garnished with a little chopped lovage.
Serves 4-6 people.

CELERY, RED PEPPER AND FENNEL SALAD (VEGETARIAN)

* Few stalks Celery
* 1 Red Pepper
* 1 Yellow or Green Pepper
* 1 Bulb Fennel
* 4oz (100 grams) Cooked Kidney Beans
* 3oz (75 grams) Hazelnuts
* 3oz (75 grams) Brazil Nuts
* 2oz (50 grams) Pistachio Nuts or Peanuts
* Handful Alfalfa Sprouts
* Handful Sprouted Buckwheat Grains
* 2 Sliced Kiwi Fruits

Top and tail the bulb of fennel and slice it up horizontally. Toss all the prepared ingredients in a salad bowl and serve with a dressing of hazelnut oil with celery and fennel seeds. Obviously, don't feel that

this recipe or any other in the book has to be rigidly adhered to, if there are any ingredients you don't want, just leave them out.
Serves 2-4 people.

SARDINE OR PILCHARD SALAD

* 2 Tins of Sardines or Pilchards in Brine.
* 1 Head of Lettuce (washed and shredded)
* ½ Cucumber (sliced)
* 1 Small Kohlrabi (peeled and shredded)
* 1 Bunch Watercress (washed and roughly chopped)
* 1 Finely Chopped Leek (optional)
* 4oz (100 grams) Pecans
* 4oz (100 grams) Walnuts
* 2oz (50 grams) Sunflower Seeds
* Handful Fresh Thyme (roughly chopped)
* Little Winter Savoury (roughly chopped)
* Few sprigs Chopped Mint
* Walnut Oil or Sunflower Oil

Marinade the herbs in a small amount of oil. Toss all the prepared salad ingredients in a bowl. Pour over the walnut or sunflower oil and herb dressing and serve with the drained fish. Serves 2-4 people.

PEAR AND WALNUT SALAD (VEGETARIAN)

* 4 Firm but ripe Pears
* 1 Head of Lettuce (washed and shredded)
* ½ Cucumber (sliced)
* 6oz (150 grams) Dried Unsulphured Apricots (soaked overnight)
* 4oz (100 grams) Walnut Halves
* 4oz (100 grams) Pecans
* 2oz (50 grams) Sunflower Seeds
* Bunch of Watercress
* 8oz Feta or Goats' Cheese (cut into cubes)
* Tarragon, Mint and Thyme (to taste)
* Walnut Oil

Wash and prepare all the ingredients apart from the pears, herbs and walnut oil. Toss them together in a salad bowl. Peel and quarter the pears. Cut out the cores and any stringy bits. Add the fruit to the rest of the ingredients and drizzle over the chopped herbs and walnut oil. This can be served as a starter or an accompaniment to a meat or fish course. Serves 4 people.

TOMATO AND LIMA SALAD (VEGETARIAN)

* 4 Large chopped Tomatoes
* 8oz (200 grams) Cooked or Tinned Lima Beans
* 1 small chopped Onion (optional)
* 4oz (100 grams) Cashew Nuts
* 2oz Sesame Seeds
* 1 Small Bulb of Celeriac finely chopped or grated
* 4oz (100 grams) Sprouted Mung Beans
* 4oz (100 grams) Sprouted Chickpeas
* 6 Boiled and sliced Quail's Eggs (optional)
* Few pitted olives (optional)
* Few sprigs of Coriander and Parsley
* Olive or Sesame Oil

Chop the coriander and parsley very finely and place in a small bowl with some olive or sesame oil and leave for about an hour in the fridge. Toss all the prepared ingredients together in a large salad bowl pour over the herb and oil dressing and serve. Serves 4 people.

TOFU STIR FRY (VEGETARIAN)

* 250 grams Firm Tofu (diced)
* 1 Red Pepper (de-seeded and diced)
* 1 Green or Yellow Pepper (de-seeded and diced)
* 1 Tamarillo (Tree Tomato sliced)
* 8oz (200 grams) Green Beans (sliced thinly)
* 1 Bulb Fennel (sliced thinly across the grain)
* Handful Alfalfa Sprouts
* 2 Stalks Celery (finely chopped)
* Ground Cardamon (to taste)
* Celery Seeds (to taste)

* Fennel Seeds (to taste)
* Fresh Lime Juice (to taste)
* Grated Root Ginger (to taste)
* Turmeric (to taste)
* Little chopped Dill
* Little chopped Lovage
* 3-4oz (75-100 grams) Pistachio Nuts (optional)

Combine all ingredients in a wok or heavy saucepan and fry in your choice of oil. Fry quickly for a few minutes until everything is heated through and serve. Serves 4 people.

BUCKWHEAT AND SOYA FLOUR PASTRY QUICHE (VEGETARIAN)

For the pastry:

* 4oz (100 grams) Buckwheat Flour
* 4oz (100 grams) Full Fat Soya Flour
* 3/4 Teaspoon Cream of Tartar
* 1/4 Teaspoon Bicarbonate of Soda
* 4oz Soya Margarine

For the Filling:

* 140 grams (½ block) Firm Tofu, (blended with enough soya milk to form a very thick cream)
* 2 Spring Onions (chopped finely)
* 1 Courgette (sliced)
* ½ Bulb of Fennel (sliced)
* ½ Red Pepper (de-seeded and chopped)
* 1 Tomato (sliced)
* Little chopped Lovage (optional)
* Celery Seeds (to taste)
* Fennel Seeds (to taste)

Put all the ingredients for the pastry into a bowl and rub to breadcrumbs. Add enough filtered water to form a stiff dough. This type of pastry is infuriating to roll out. It is much easier to place the ball of pastry in the centre of a 10" quiche dish and press it out carefully and coax it gently up the sides. I don't even bother to bake it blind. I've found that it dries out too quickly. Just arrange the sliced and chopped vegetables in the bottom, pour the soya and tofu blend over it and pop it in a medium oven until firm and golden brown on top. Lower the oven temperature as it starts to go brown, otherwise the outside will burn before it is properly set in the middle. (Bake for at least 50 minutes in a fan oven, even longer in a conventional one). Serves 4-6 people.

RYE FLOUR PANCAKES

* 4oz (100 grams) Rye Flour (or your choice)
* 2 Free Range Hens' Eggs
* Sheep or Goats' Milk or Filtered Water
* Sunflower Oil

Make a batter in the usual way. Heat the oil in a frying pan and pour in enough batter to coat the bottom. Cook for a couple of minutes each side and serve with your choice of fruits, either raw, or stewed and perhaps sweetened with honey. You may like to try a savoury version with mushrooms, leeks, garlic, walnuts and a feta cheese sauce, see below. Makes 4-5 pancakes.

FETA CHEESE SAUCE

* 1 Pint (500 ml) Sheep or Goats' Milk
* 2oz (50 grams) Tapioca Flour
* 4oz (100 grams) Feta or Goats' Cheese

Mix the tapioca flour to a smooth paste with a little of the milk in a heavy bottomed saucepan. Gradually add the rest of the milk and the grated cheese. Stir constantly as you bring it to the boil. Lower the heat and keep stirring until it thickens. As well as a savoury filling for pancakes, this basic sauce can also be used with fish.

TURKEY STIR FRY

* 1lb (400 grams) Turkey Breast Strips
* 1 Bulb Fennel (chopped finely)
* 4 Stalks Celery (chopped finely)

*	1 Red Pepper (de-seeded and diced)
*	1 Yellow Pepper (de-seeded and diced)
*	½lb (200 grams) sliced Green Beans
*	2oz (50 grams) Alfalfa Sprouts
*	½ Teaspoon Celery Seeds
*	2 or 3 crushed Cardamon Pods
*	Turmeric (to taste)
*	Grated Root Ginger (to taste)
*	Oil of your choice

Heat the oil in a wok or heavy bottomed saucepan. Add the turkey strips and cook on a fairly high heat for a few minutes whilst you prepare all the other ingredients. Lower the heat and add everything else to the pan. Continue cooking until the meat is tender. Serve at once with wild rice if liked and tolerated.
Serves 4 people.

CHICKEN KIEV

*	4 Chicken Breasts
*	2-3 Cloves of Garlic (crushed)
*	Handful Finely Chopped Thyme
*	1 Finely Chopped Leek
*	Sunflower Margarine

Slit the chicken breasts open to form pockets. Mix the garlic, thyme and leeks with the sunflower margarine and stuff into the pockets. Place into an ovenproof dish and brush with sunflower oil. Cover and roast in a moderate oven until golden brown. Try mixing some goats' or sheep yoghurt with the juices to make a creamy sauce. Garnish with watercress and serve with your choice of vegetables of the day.
Serves 4 people

CROWN OF LAMB WITH APRICOT STUFFING

* A loin of Lamb consisting of about 12 Chops
* 8oz (200 grams) Unsulphured Dried Apricots (soaked overnight and chopped roughly)
* 8oz (200 grams) Kohlrabi (grated)
8 1 Small Leek (finely chopped)
* Few Sprigs of fresh Thyme
* Few Sprigs of Winter Savoury
* Few Sprigs Rosemary
* 4oz (100 grams) Lamb's Liver (cut into strips and lightly fried in walnut oil - optional)
* 4oz (100 grams) Mushrooms (washed, sliced and lightly fried)
* 2oz (50 grams) Chopped Walnuts (optional)
* 2oz (50 grams) Chopped Pecans (optional)
* 1oz (25 grams) Sunflower Seeds
* 1oz (25 grams) Pumpkin Seeds

Trim the fat from the meat and scrape back the flesh from the top one and a half to two inches of bone. Bend the joint round to form a circle. Get your butcher to cut halfway through each chop so it is easier to bend. The skinside should be facing inwards, obviously, so that the sides are concave. Secure with string or meat skewers. Place in a roasting dish and baste with either sunflower or walnut oil, and cook in a moderate oven until the meat is tender. Mix together all the ingredients for the stuffing which should be added to the meat cavity at least half an hour before the meat is ready. Sprinkle with chopped mint and serve with your choice of vegetables and other herbs.
Serves 6-8 people.

PEAR AND TAPIOCA CUSTARD

* 2 Tins of Pears in Natural Juice
* 1 Tablespoon Tapioca Flour

Pour some of the pear juice into a heavy bottomed saucepan. Add the tapioca flour and stir until well blended and dissolved. Put the rest of the pears and juice in a blender and blend until smooth. Add to the slaked tapioca, turn up the heat stirring constantly until the mixture thickens. Serve either on its own or with stewed unsulphured figs or other fruits and maybe a little live yoghurt if liked.

APRICOT AND TAPIOCA CUSTARD

* 1lb (400 grams) Unsulphured Apricots (soaked overnight in boiled filtered water)
* 1 Tablespoon Tapioca Flour
* Honey (to taste)

Stew the apricots in their liquor until tender and allow to cool. Slake the tapioca flour with enough of the liquor to make a smooth runny paste. Blend the cooled apricots in a blender until smooth and add the tapioca paste. Return to the heat stirring constantly until the mixture comes to the boil and thickens. Remove from the heat and sweeten with honey to taste. Serve with a little live yoghurt if liked.

MELON AND APRICOT FRUIT SALAD

* 1 Ripe Melon (peeled, de-seeded and cubed)
* 8oz (200 grams) Dried, Unsulphured Apricots (soaked overnight in boiled filtered water)
* 2 or 3 Ripe Pears (peeled and sliced or tinned in own juice)
* 8oz (200 grams) Fresh Raspberries (or frozen thawed overnight)
* 8oz (200 grams) Loganberries (if available)

Toss all ingredients together in a bowl, pour over some pure fruit juice of the day and serve.

RYE FLOUR BASIC CAKE MIXTURE

* 8oz (200 grams) Rye Flour
* 8oz (200 grams) Sunflower Margarine
* 8oz (200 grams) Beet Sugar (or honey to taste)
* 4 Free Range Hens' Eggs (or 1 rounded dessertspoonful Tapioca Flour)

* 1 Rounded Teaspoonful Cream of Tartar
* 1 Level Teaspoonful Bicarbonate of Soda

Cream margarine and sugar or honey. If using eggs crack them in one at a time and beat well before adding the flour. If using tapioca flour, sift it with the rye flour and raising agents and fold it into the beaten margarine and sugar, add enough filtered water to obtain a good dropping consistency. Divide the mixture between two 8" cake tins and bake in a moderate oven until golden brown and firm to the touch.

Variations

APRICOT AND WALNUT CAKE

Add 4oz (100 grams) chopped, unsulphured apricots that have been soaked overnight and 4oz (100 grams) chopped walnuts to the basic cake mixture and divide between two loaf tins, bake as main recipe.

RASPBERRY MUFFINS

Add 8oz (200 grams) fresh or frozen and defrosted raspberries to the basic cake mixture, divide into bun cases and bake in a moderate oven.

STEAMED FIG OR APRICOT PUDDING

About a pound (400 grams) unsulphured apricots or figs soaked overnight then stewed in their own liquor, sweetened to taste with either beet sugar or honey. Place in a pyrex type pudding basin cover with half the quantity of the basic cake mixture, cover with paper or tin foil and steam for around one and a half hours until well risen and spongy. Serve with apricot and tapioca custard.

OIL CARAWAY CAKE

* Soya Margarine for greasing tin
* 8oz (200 grams) Barley Flour
* 1 Heaped Teaspoon Cream of Tartar
* 1 Level Teaspoon Bicarbonate of Soda

* ½ oz Caraway Seeds
* 4oz (100 grams) Fructose
* 1 Tablespoon Treacle
* 2 Eggs (or equivalent replacer eg. 1 rounded dessertspoon Tapioca Flour)
* 5 fl oz Oil of your choice
* 2 fl oz Filtered Water

Grease and flour 2 x 7" round cake tins. Sift all dry ingredients into a bowl, blend together the eggs, oil, warmed treacle and water and pour into the bowl stir all ingredients well until blended. Divide between the two tins and bake in a moderate oven for about 40 minutes, (less in a fan oven) until the cakes have shrunk away from the sides of the tins.

Alternatives to caraway seeds: you can use unsulphured dried fruits of your choice, or perhaps freshly chopped apple and cinnamon, or try omitting the water and add the grated rind and juice of an orange, lemon or lime with a little freshly grated root ginger.

COCONUT ICE

* 10 fl oz (250 ml) Coconut Milk
* 1 Block Creamed Coconut
* 8oz (200 grams) Desiccated Coconut (unsulphured)
* Maple Syrup or Date Sugar (to taste)
* 2 Sachets Vegegel

Pour the coconut milk into a heavy bottomed saucepan and add the vegegel and block of creamed coconut bring slowly to the boil stirring constantly until the creamed coconut has melted, by which time the vegegel will be starting to thicken. Add maple syrup or date sugar at this stage and beat in the desiccated coconut. Turn out into a large rectangular dish and allow to set before cutting into squares.

FRUIT SALAD

* 1 Ripe Melon (peeled, de-seeded and cubed)

* 8oz (200 grams) Dried Unsulphured Apricots (soaked overnight)
* 2 or 3 Ripe Pears (peeled and sliced or tinned in natural juice)
* 8oz (200 grams) Fresh Raspberries (or defrosted frozen)
* 8oz (200 grams) Loganberries (if available, if not use more raspberries)

Toss all ingredients together in a large bowl with some pure pear juice and serve. Serves 6-8 people.

CHAPTER NINE

COOKING SUBSTITUTES

MILK Fruit Juice, vegetable puree and vegetable cooking water all work reasonably well in cooking and baking in place of milk. Test sheep or goat's milk to see if you are allergic to it and if not use it occasionally. Like all milks it tends to separate when frozen so where possible, buy it fresh.
Soya milk has a less pleasant flavour, but is good in rice puddings, custards etc.
Coffee Mate and Coffee Compliment may be used, (but test to be sure it suits you)
Raw potato water may be used instead of milk in any recipe.
To make it: Dice potato into a blender and add warm water, (about ½ cup) and blend. There is now a good range of plant milks available in most healthfood shops. Such as oat milk, rice milk, millet milk and almond milk which may be used on the rotation diet.

WHIPPED CREAM

Add a sliced banana to one beaten egg white. Beat until stiff and the banana will dissolve. Use immediately or it will discolour and separate.

BUTTER

Use melted animal fat of any kind: Poultry fat has a nice flavour but goose and duck are softer and moister than butter: Pork and beef fat are about the same in texture; lamb fat is harder and stays very firm at room temperature.
Vegetable oils can be used too, but they can be too thin and dry for some recipes (if you can tolerate glycerine, which is hygroscopic, therefore attracting moisture, you may be able to add a dessertspoonful to the recipe to compensate for the

dryness or add fruit puree to the mixture to add both fibre and moisture)

EGG To give body and stickiness use: apple or other fruit sauce, pureed cooked, starch vegetables, flaxseed water mixture; cottage cheese or soured milk, or nut butter. One teaspoon of baking powder for each egg left out will give the rising power of one egg, but won't keep the baked goods from falling as an egg will because it lacks the egg's cohesive properties (body and stickiness). I have often used tapioca flour, sago flour and arrowroot as egg substitutes and these all work reasonably well, they provide some degree of stickiness and set quite well. You could also try cornflour or potato starch. A raised dessertspoonful or any of these starches to 9oz of flour will work quite well.

SUGAR

Honey, sorghum and maple syrup can be substituted, but the other liquids in the recipe must be decreased. 1/4 cup for each. cup of honey, maple or sorghum. Honey is 2½ times sweeter than sugar, so keep this in mind when substituting. A honey/fat combination turns out better if not blended like a sugar/fat combination, so a honey recipe is often more successful. See honey recipe books for detailed honey use, but bear in mind the need to rotate foods as much as possible. When no liquid is called for, (as in some candy recipes) try adding something granular (nuts or grains for instance). Ordinary recipes using sugar, can be used by substituting fructose, obtainable from the diabetic counters of high street supermarkets.
Sorbitol (available from Boots) can be used instead of fructose, and is rather like icing sugar. Limit intake however, as too much can have a laxative effect! Sorbitol is good for butter cream icing. It can be flavoured with pure flavourings - mint is lovely, it also costs a lost less than fructose.

GRAIN Do not use rye, corn, barley, malt flour or millet as a substitute wheat. Flours other than rye, wheat and barley are low in gluten and do not stick together very well. They tend to collapse easily. Shredded raw starch vegetables such as carrots, potatoes, parsnips, artichokes, young turnips, kohlrabi, squash or sweet potatoes, will help to provide fibre to hold the mixture together.

WHEAT

(Substitutes for one cup of wheat flour)

3-4 Cup Corn Starch	7/8 Cup Buckwheat
7/8 Cup Cornflour	7/8 Cup Rice Flour
3/4 Cup Coarse Cornmeal	1 1/3 Cup Ground Rolled Oats
1 Scant Cup Fine Cornmeal	3/4 Cup Soya Flour
3/8 Cup Potato Flour	½ Cup Oatmeal (finely ground)
3/4 Cup Sago Flour	

Products baked with these flours require long, slow baking. See manufacturers recipes for further details. Source of above information: Nutrition Associates, Galtres House, Lysander Close, Clifton Moorgate, York.

TRI-SALTS

* 2 Parts Potassium Bicarbonate
* 3 Parts Sodium Bicarbonate
* 1 Part Calcium Carbonate

Sieve all the ingredients together, (you may need to do this outside or wear a dust mask as it can make you sneeze a lot). Use one teaspoon of the above mixture to 1/4-½ teaspoon powdered vitamin C in a third of a tumbler full of filtered water to alleviate allergic reactions such as headaches, nausea, chronic heartburn etc. The sooner you take the tri-salts after a suspect food the better it works to lessen the symptoms. Source Airedale Allergy Centre, Nr Keighley.

CHAPTER TEN

ORGANIC FOOD

Many shops and supermarkets offer organic food for sale, but how does the consumer know that the food sold really is organic? Producers could argue that all food is organic because it comes from plants and animals. However, for the past fifty years or so, the term has been used to describe food grown without most artificial fertilizers or pesticides and in a way that makes the most of natural fertilizers, thus ensuring the life and good condition of the soil.

Animals are kept in humane ways which minimise the need for medicines and hormone treatments.

As consumers, we're entitled to expect that everything in our diet has been produced with the minimum of interference from man. But it would be naive to expect the use of artificial fertlizers and pesticides to cease when their use increases production and thus profits for the producers.

There are a number of terms which can be used to describe food which has been grown in a traditional or environmentally friendly way. However, 'organic' is the only one subject to a European Community and national regulation.

DEFINITION OF ORGANIC FARMING

'Organic production systems are designed to produce optimum quantities of food of high nutritional quality by using management practices which avoid the use of agro-chemical inputs and which minimise damage to the environment and wildlife.'

'The principle includes:-

* Working with natural systems rather than seeking to dominate them.
* The encouragement of biological cycles involving micro-organisms, soil flora and fauna, plants and animals.
* The maintenance of valuable existing landscape features and adequate habitats for the production of wildlife with particular regard for endangered species.

* Careful attention to animal welfare considerations.
* The avoidance of pollution.
* Consideration for the wider social and ecological impact of the farming system.'

Extract from the UK Register Of Organic Food Standards. UKROFS Standards Of Organic Food Production.

In 1993 European Regulation governing the term 'Organic' farming became effective. This describes the inputs and practices which may be used in organic farming and growing and the inspection system which must be put in place to ensure this.

The regulation also applies to processing aids and all ingredients in organic foods. So all food grown as organic must come from growers, processors, or importers who are registered and subject to regular inspection.

In the United Kingdom the regulation is administered by the United Kingdom Register of Organic Food Standards - UKROFS. Which consists of an independent Board appointed by Agriculture Ministers which is assisted by a small Secretariat provided by the Ministry of Agriculture, Fisheries and Food. Its job is to ensure that the EC Regulations are properly applied in the UK by the various bodies which register organic farmers and processors.

It is illegal to offer food for sale as organic unless it has been produced in full conformity with the EC Regulations by registered producers. So the word 'organic' on the label or used by the shopkeeper is your guarantee that it has been organically produced. 'Source: Ministry Of Agriculture Fisheries and Food.
If you want to know more contact:
United Kingdom Register
Of Organic Food Standards
Room 320c
Nobel House
17 Smith Square
London
SW1P 3JR
Tel 0207 238 5781

CHAPTER ELEVEN

VITAMINS AND MINERALS

Vitamin A	Liver, Oily fish, (eg herrings) full-fat milk and dairy products, butter, margarine, carrots, green leafy vegetables, peaches, nectarines and dried apricots. Pregnant women have been advised to avoid foods rich in Vitamin A, especially liver and liver products.
Functions:	Needed for healthy skin and eyes, good digestion, respiration, healthy glands and bowel functions. Deficiency can lead to hay fever, poor co-ordination, allergies, impaired bone growth, breathing problems, sore mouth and gums and general susceptibility to disease.
The B Group Vitamins:	Meat, (particularly liver and kidney) oily fish, (eg Herrings), wholemeal and white bread, whole grain cereals, fortified breakfast cereals, pulses, nuts and yeast extract. Vitamin B2 (Riboflavin) and Vitamin B12 are also found in full and low-fat dairy products and eggs. Most sources of Vitamin B12 (with the exception of yeast extract) are of animal origin and vegans and vegetarians may need supplements.
Functions:	Vitamin B1 (THIAMINE) - Necessary for the proper functioning of the immune system, nervous system, heart and lungs also for healthy muscles. Deficiency leads to weaknesses, in these systems and impaired growth in young children. Vitamin B2 (RIBOFLAVIN) - Essential for building and maintaining body tissues. Signs of deficiency are sensitivity to sunlight, sore tongue and sores at the corner of the mouth.

Vitamin B3 (NIACIN, NICOTINIC ACID, NICOTINAMIDE) Essential for converting food into energy; necessary for the central nervous system, healthy appetite and good skin condition. Deficiency can lead to rashes, mouth ulcers, skin lesions and diarrhoea.

Vitamin B5 (PANTOTHENIC ACID) Necessary for tissue growth and repair, healthy skin and hair. Signs of deficiency are muscle cramps and fatigue.

Vitamin B6 (PYRIDOXINE) Important for healthy teeth and gums, the maintenance of healthy blood vessels, red blood cells and the central nervous system. Essential for the conversion of foods into energy. Deficiency can cause depression, anaemia, skin disorders, irritability and diarrhoea.

Vitamin B12 (CYANOCOBALAMIN) Necessary for healthy blood function; helps to promote a healthy nervous system and is very important for normal growth in children. Deficiency can result in Pernicious Anaemia.

Folate: Liver, yeast extracts and leafy green vegetables (eg cabbage)

Folic Acid is particularly important in pre-conception and early pregnancy.

Functions: Folic acid is closely linked with Vitamin B12 and the two are needed for the production of healthy blood cells. If the two are in short supply blood cells do not mature and divide as they should, but increase in size and get fewer in number - a condition known as megaloblastic anaemia. It is not advisable to take folic acid on its own since this may mask a Vitamin B12 deficiency. Studies have shown that giving pregnant women vitamin supplements including folic acid reduces the likelihood of disorders such as Spina Bifida.

Vitamin C	(ASCORBIC ACID) Fresh and frozen fruit and vegetables, particularly citrus fruits, soft drinks, fruit juice, green vegetables and salad vegetables. Also found in potatoes and in products fortified with Vitamin C.
Functions:	Important for the development and maintenance of a healthy immune system. Also for the health of the connective tissues and muscles, sex organs and glandular tissues. It also aids the absorption of protein and calcium. Deficiency leads to bleeding gums, wounds that don't heal very easily or quickly, eye problems and a low resistance to infections. Also said to be of benefit in treating infections and diseases including cancer.
Vitamin D	(CALCIFEROL) Main source is the action of sunlight on the skin. Few food sources: oily fish (eg mackerel or herrings) eggs, margarine and fortified breakfast cereals.
Functions:	Essential for the balance of phosphorus and calcium, for a healthy heart, muscles and stable nervous system. Deficiency leads to heart and muscles becoming weak and bone and teeth problems.
Vitamin E	(TOCOPHEROL) Vegetable oils, eggs, whole-grain cereals and leafy green vegetables, (eg cabbage)
Functions:	Vital for healthy heart and liver and efficient glandular system deficiency leads to poor muscle tone and inadequate supply of oxygen to the tissues.
BIOTIN (Vitamin H)	Wholewheat, milk and dairy products, eggs, honey, molasses, yeast, herrings and cod's roe, kidney, liver, oysters, oatmeal and raisins.

Functions:	Important for the synthesis of proteins and necessary for healthy mucus membranes, cardiovascular system, red blood cells and skin. Deficiency can lead to muscle pain and dermatitis.
Vitamin K	(PHYTOMENADIONE, PHYLLOQUINONE) Whole-grain cereals and leafy green vegetables.
Functions:	Essential for the blood to ensure clotting ability.

MINERAL SOURCES

Calcium	Full and low fat dairy products, canned fish, (eg sardines) white bread, pulses (including baked beans) leafy green vegetables and dried fruit.
Functions:	Necessary for healthy teeth and bones. Calcium deficiency can lead to rickets, brittle bones and rheumatic pains during old age.
Iron	Meat, (particularly offal) green leafy vegetables, wholemeal bread, pulses, eggs and dried fruit.
Functions:	Iron is a constituent of haemoglobin, which carries oxygen round the bloodstream. As well as leading to anaemia, deficiency can contribute to poor muscle tone and weakness, impaired metabolism and coldness in the hands and feet. Lassitude and poor learning ability can be a sign of deficiency.
Fluoride	Seafood and tea. Also green leafy vegetables such as broccoli and cabbage, cauliflower, calabrese, cress, kale, spring greens, swede, turnip and garlic. In some areas tap water also contains fluoride; as do some brands of toothpaste of course.
Functions:	Deficiency can lead to dental and skin problems, anaemia and headaches. However, there is controversy at the moment about excess use of fluoride and its addition to tapwater and long term possible health risks.

Selenium — Many cereals (including bread) meat, liver, brown rice, garlic, yeast, raw cane sugar, eggs and fish.

Functions: Necessary for normal liver function, selenium is one of the most powerful anti-oxidants known. When used in conjunction with Vitamin E, it appears to increase the efficiency and effectiveness of the vitamin in its various roles. Selenium is also needed for fertility.

Other minerals which are vital to our good health and wellbeing include, iodine, zinc, copper, magnesium and chromium. Though they are needed in tiny amounts and they are present in such a wide range of foods, the MAFF has found that many people are now deficient in their intakes of selenium and zinc.

Functions: IODINE - Necessary for the normal functioning of the thyroid gland. Helps to promote immune system and reduces nervous tension and irritability.

ZINC: There is no doubt that zinc deficiency will reduce the function of the immune system and impair the efficiency of other defence mechanisms. It has been found to be important in food allergies, preventing hair loss, infertility and poor healing of wounds. It also affects the ability to taste and helps with muscle co-ordination. Found in all meat, poultry and many seafoods, as well as nuts, legumes and pulses, cereals, eggs, cheese, yeast, sweetcorn and tomato puree.

COPPER: Found in such a wide variety of foods that supplements are rarely needed. It aids the formation of red blood cells in conjunction with iron and is also necessary for healthy bone growth. Deficiency can lead to diarrhoea and changes of hair colour and texture.

MAGNESIUM: An important aid in the detoxification of the body. It plays an important part in helping the brain, muscles and nerves to relax and so aids the ability to get a good night's sleep. It also contributes to the utilisation of protein. Found in many foods including wheat and other cereals, molasses, various nuts, pulses and seeds, alfalfa, beansprouts, seafoods, dried fruits such as apricots, figs, raisins and dates. Watercress, spinach, sweetcorn and rooibosch tea to name but a few.

CHROMIUM: Important trace element needed during the metabolism of carbohydrates, lack of it is thought to contribute to diabetes. Found in: Beef, calf liver, brewer's yeast, whole grain cereals, oysters and potatoes.

It is important to ensure that any diet is nutritionally adequate and that you are not relying heavily on supplements, rather than a well balanced diet with sufficient intake of vitamins, minerals and trace elements as well as proteins and carbohydrates. As I said earlier in the book, it is important to have your GP's support and referral to a qualified State Registered Dietician with an in-depth knowledge of allergies before attempting to change a child's diet, as the child could easily become deficient in vital nutrients needed for growth and development.

CHAPTER TWELVE

FOOD FAMILIES

Agar	Carrageenan, Kelp
Brewer's Yeast	Baker's Yeast, Mushrooms, Truffle
Barley	Bamboo Shoots, Corn, Malt, Millet, Oat, Rice, Rye, Sugar Cane (Molasses) Wheat (Bran, Bulgar) Wild Rice, Sorghum.
Coconut	Date, Palm, Sago Starch
Pineapple	Single Member
Asparagus	Chives, Garlic, Leek, Onion, Shallot
Chinese Potato	(Yam) (Single Member)
Saffron	Saffron (Single Member)
Banana	Plantain, Ginger, Arrowroot, Vanilla, Turmeric
Beechnut	Chestnut
Beet	Chard, Spinach, Sugar Beet, Beetroot, Good King Henry, Orach
Strawberry	Blackberry, Boysenberry, Loganberry, Raspberry
Hazelnut	Wintergreen
Buckwheat	Rhubarb, Sorrel
Coriander	Carrot, Angelica, Caraway, Celery, Cumin, Chervil, Parsley, Dill, Fennel, Parsnip
Mango	Cashew, Pistachio
Citrus	Orange, Grapefruit, Lemon, Lime, Citron, Mandarin, Tangerine, Kumquat, Satsuma
Composites	Camomile, Artichoke, Dandelion, Chicory, Lettuce, Endive, Sunflower, Safflower, Tarragon, Salsify
Courgettes	Cucumber, Gherkin, Melon, (Honeydew) Watermelon, Squash, Pumpkin
Grape	Raisin, Cream of Tartar
Avocado	Bayleaf, Sassafras, Cinnamon
Legumes	Peas, Beans, Lentils, Liquorice, Peanut, Soya, Tapioca, Senna Carob, Chickpea, Fenugreek, Tamarind, Alfalfa
Coffee	Coffee (Single Member)

Mint	Mint, Applemint, Bergamot, Basil, Oregano, Lavender, Lemon Balm, Marjoram, Rosemary, Thyme, Sage, Pineapple Sage, Spearmint
Fig	Breadfruit, Mulberry, Hop
Brassica	Cabbage, Brussels Sprouts, Broccoli, Cauliflower, Chinese Leaves, Kale, Cress, Horseradish, Kohlrabi, Radish, Turnip, Mustard, Watercress
Olive	Olive (Single Member)
Pomegranate	Grenadine
Potato	Aubergine, (eggplant) Tomato, Potato, Pepper, Chilli Pepper, Tobacco, Tree Tomato (Tamarillo) Cayenne, Paprika, Pimento, Chilli Powder (Order - Nightshades)
Apple	Crabapple, Pear, Cider, Calvados, Rosehip
Almond	Apricot, Cherry, Peach, Nectarine, Plum, Prune, Sloe, Quince
Gooseberry	Red and Blackcurrants
Cocoa	Chocolate, Cola
Tea	Tea (Single Member)
Verbena	Lemon Verbena
Walnut	Butternut, Hickory Nut, Pecan
Cranberry	Cranberry (Single Member)
Sharron Fruit	(Persimmon) Single Member
Kiwi	(Chinese Gooseberry) Single Member
Passion Fruit	(Grenadilla) Single Member
Lychee	Lychee (Single Member)
Maple Syrup	Maple Syrup (Single Member)
Brazil Nut	Brazil Nut (Single Member)
Sweet Potato	Sweet Potato (Single Member)
Honey	Honey (Single Member)
Borage	Comfrey
Okra	Hibiscus
Papaya	Papaya (Single Member)
Mace	Nutmeg

BIRDS

Pigeon	Dove, Wood Pigeon

Duck	Goose
Partridge	Grouse
Guinea Fowl	Guinea Fowl and Eggs (Single Member)
Chicken	Pheasant, Chicken, Hen's Eggs, Quail and Eggs
Turkey	Turkey (Single Member)
Ostrich	Ostrich (Single Member)

MAMMALS

Bovine	Beef, Milk and Dairy Products, Veal, Offal, Tongue, Tripe Gelatine, Suet, Lactose, Casein, Buffalo, Bison, Goat Meat, Goat Milk, Yoghurt and Cheese, Lamb, Liver and Kidney, Mutton, Sheep Milk, Yoghurt and Cheese
Deer	Reindeer, Moose, Caribou, Elk and Venison
Pig	Pork, Wild Boar, Pigs' Liver and Kidneys
Hare	Rabbit

SEA FOOD

Crustaceans	Lobster, Crab, Shrimp, Crayfish, Prawn
Octopus	Octopus
Molluscs	Cockles, Mussels, Oysters, Clams, Abalone, Scallop, Squid, Snail

FRESH WATER FISH

Shad	Herring
Bass	Bass, Yellow Bass, White Perch
Carp	Minnow and Chub
Red Snapper	Yellow Perch
Pickerel	Pike
Trout	Salmon
Smelt	Smelt (Single Member)
White Fish	White Fish (Single Member)
Sunfish	Black Bass
Sturgeon	Caviar, Sturgeon

SALTWATER FISH

Flounder	Dab, Flounder, Halibut, Sole, Plaice, Turbot
Anchovy	Anchovy (Single Member)
Eel	Eel (Single Member)
Haddock	Cod, Cod Liver Oil, Pollock, Hake
Herring	Sardine, Pilchard
Tuna	Mackerel, Tuna, Bonito, Skipjack
Red Mullet	Grey Mullet
Sea Bream	Porgy, Bream
Sea Trout	Salmon
Rock Fish	Ocean perch, Scorpionfish
Grouper	Sea Bass
Sea Catfish	Catfish (Single Member)
White Bait	White Bait (Single Member)

CHAPTER THIRTEEN

APPENDIX I

ACKNOWLEDGEMENTS

I would like to take this opportunity to offer my heartfelt thanks to all the doctors who have helped me and my family. Firstly our GP, Dr Roger Kaufmann who has always been so kind, patient and willing to learn and offer his help and support, especially on those occasions, before Howard was treated at Airedale, when the stomach pains were so bad we had to call him out at all ungodly hours to administer morphine.

I would also like to thank Dr Kate Ward, the paediatric allergy specialist who treated Peter at Airedale General Hospital. She and her Dietician, Angela Freeman, make a great team and I am sure I can speak for many parents when I offer them my thanks and gratitude for my son's good health.

My thanks also to Dr Honor Anthony for her help and guidance in reading through this book and offering her much needed advice and also for initially diagnosing Howard's illness and organising his admission to Airedale Allergy Centre.

My thanks also to Dr Jonathan Maberly and his team of staff at that unique clinic.

Airedale Allergy Centre was a purpose built unit, built in the grounds of Dr Maberly's house at Steeton, near Keighley. It was designed and built to Dr Maberly's specifications. The air was triple filtered and so was the water. The only cleaning solutions allowed were borax and bicarbonate of soda. (Though the place was absolutely spotlessly clean). The floors were either plain hardwood or tiles. Curtains, soft furnishings and bedding were in unbleached cottons and calico. Patients were only allowed simple, unfragranced soap and shampoo and used bicarbonate of soda to clean their teeth.

Visitors were banned from smoking, wearing make up, perfumes, hair sprays, deodorants, or aftershaves which could upset sensitive patients. They were also required to wear cotton over gowns and cotton 'slippers' instead of their outdoor shoes. This may sound extreme to you, but the people who were ill enough to need treating there were likely to react to twentieth century perfumes, cosmetics and synthetic fibres, and so visitors had to respect this. Newspapers, books and magazines were also banned because patients are often sensitive to the smell of the printer's ink and the glossy finish on the paper. (The clinic had a substantial stock of old books and magazines that had lost their smell).

The clinic was run by a highly skilled team of staff, dedicated to the care and ultimate recovery of their patients. When the allergens provoking ill health had been identified, patients were taught how to reduce their exposure to them, and protected using one of the low dose desensitisation methods, neutralisation. This allowed the patients to eat foods to which they were intolerant, but only one day in four for the first few months, sometimes longer.

The success rate was impressively high and I personally cannot praise them enough.

Over the years since it opened, a great many people have regained their health and vitality as a result of the unique treatment they have received there and I cannot express how sad I feel at the thought of its closure. It will still be open to out-patients but the clinic cannot continue to admit in-patients anymore due to a hiatus in NHS funding and this side of the practice closed from April 1999. New address for Airedale Allergy Centre (Out-patients only): 41 Devonshire Street, Keighley, BD21 2BH. Telephone 01535 603966 (Dr. Econs).

My thanks also go to Dr Damien Downing and his staff at Nutrition Associates in York.

Dr Downing used the cytotoxic test and another low dose desensitisation method, Enzyme Potentiated Desensitisation (EPD) a pioneering type of allergy treatment developed and refined by Dr Len McEwen over the past thirty years.

Dr Downing's address is as follows:

Nutrition Associates
Galtrse House
Lysander Close
Clifton Moorgate
York
YO3 4XB
Tel 01904 691590
or
Bio Lab Medical Unit
The Stone House
9 Weymouth Street
London
WIN 3FF
Tel 0207 636 5959

USEFUL NAMES AND ADDRESSES OF SUPPLIERS

AIR FILTER DEHUMIDIFIERS

Anatomia Air Filters (now called the AC300) available from Ascot-Heath, (Pennine) Ltd. Throstle Bank, Clitheroe, Lancs. Tel 0200 23611

Healthy House, Cold Harbour, Ruscombe, Stroud, Gloucester GL6 4DA Tel 0453 752216 (they stock a range of airfilters/dehumidifiers/dust-mite proof bedding/low odour paints/self help books for allergy sufferers etc. By mail order, catalogue supplied on request).

Allerayde 42 Kirkgate, Newark, NG24 1AB Tel 0636 613444 (air cleaners)

Medivac, (Tailormaid Products)18a Water Lane, Wilmslow, Cheshire, SK9 5AA Tel 0626 539401 Air filters/dehumidifiers/allergy vacuum cleaners.

Air Improvement Centre Ltd. 23 Denbigh Street, London SW1V 2HF Tel 0171 834 2834. They stock a wide range of filters and dehumidifiers.

NSA UK Ltd. NSA House 1 Reform Road, Maidenhead, Berkshire, SL6 8BY Tel 01628 776044 Car Air Filters and Domestic Air Cleaners/Water Filters.

VACUUM CLEANERS

There are now many different types of vacuum cleaners developed with allergy sufferers in mind. Technology in this area is improving all the time and so I feel it would be unwise to recommend one brand above another. Though the ones with a HEPA filter (High Efficiency Particulate Air Filter) are the most efficient.

BEDDING

Healthy House, Cold Harbour, Ruscombe, Stroud, Gloucester, GL6 4AD Tel 01453 752216 Mattresses and covers, pillows, bed linen etc.
Many leading high street chemists and department stores also now stock a range of dustmite proof mattress and pillow covers, check at your nearest branches for details.

WATER FILTERS

Aquamix Ltd. 20 Orville Street, Sutton, St Helens WA9 3JJ Tel 01744 716990
Activated charcoal and reverse osmosis water filter systems

Fresh Water Filter Company Ltd. Carlton House, Aylmer Road, Leytonstone, London E11 3AD Tel 0208 558 7495

PAINT VARNISHES AND ADHESIVES

Crown and Dulux Low Odour solvent free gloss paints from all major stockists.

Ronseal and Cuprinol Low Odour Water Based Varnish available at all good DIY stores.

Solvent free all purpose adhesive: Laybond Quickstick Green Colas Building Products, Riverside, Saltney, Chester CH4 8RS Tel 01244 674774

Healthy House Cold Harbour, Ruscombe, Stroud, Gloucester, GL6 4DA Tel 01453 752216. They stock a good range of low odour emulsion paints available by mail order.

TOOTHPASTE

Nelson's Homeopathic Toothpaste, Kingfisher Toothpaste or Weleda Toothpaste, herbal and salt. All available from healthfood shops and chemists.

COSMETICS

Cosmetics' ranges should be checked before purchase as the ingredients can change quite quickly. 'Simple' range of soaps, shampoos etc. fragrance free and available from most chemists and supermarkets.

Superdrug fragrance free shampoo and conditioner available at your nearest branch. Body Shop do some nice ranges but again check the labels.

CONTACT LENS CARE

Boots Preservative-free

CLEANING AGENTS

Hoover range available from health stores and some supermarkets.

Surecare washing powder and fabric conditioner, fragrance free, available from some branches of Tesco and Safeway.

Boots own brand fragrance free washing powder, fabric conditioner and washing up liquid. Available at most branches.

POLISH

Crown Products available at Sainsburys, (Yorks Old English Beeswax Furniture Polish)

ORGANIC WHOLEFOOD SUPPLIERS

Allergy Care (formerly Food Watch) 9 Corporation Street, Taunton, Somerset TA1 4AJ Tel 01823 325022 - Suppliers of specialised foods, supplements and dietary aids.

Food Watch International, Butts Pond Industrial Estate, Sturminster Newton, Dorset, DT10 1AZ Tel 01258 73356 Providing a wide range of foodstuffs, (by mail order, anywhere in the UK and abroad) especially to meet the needs of allergy sufferers and any one with dietary problems. As well as a wide range of organic foods, unusual types of flour etc they sell cleaning materials, water filters and provide advice and support to their customers.

SUMA, Dean Clough, Halifax, West Yorkshire HX3 5AN Tel 01422 45513 A range of dairy free margarines available from good health food stores (bulk orders delivered)

VITAMINS AND MINERALS

Lamberts Dietary Products Ltd. 1 Lamberts Road, Tunbridge Wells, Kent, TN2 3BQ Tel 01892 546488 Hypoallergenic range of multi-vitamins and minerals etc. (mail order catalogue available on request)

Nature's Best, FREEPOST, P O Box 1, Tunbridge Wells, TN2 3BQ
Tel 01892 34143 (mail order catalogue on request)

Nutrition Associates, Galtres House, Lyander Close, Clifton Moorgate, York YO3 AXB Tel 01904 691591. They supply a comprehensive range of hypoallergenic vitamin, mineral and other dietary supplements, both through the clinic and by mail order to established patients.

BRITISH SOCIETY FOR ALLERGY, ENVIRONMENTAL AND NUTRITIONAL MEDICINE

They will send a list of doctors specialising in allergies/environmental medicine to you if you send a SAE to the following address:
The Administrator
BSAENM
PO Box 7
Knighton
LD7 1WT

RECOMMENDED READING

Your GP may also find it useful to obtain a copy of either Effective Allergy Practice or Effective Nutritional Medicine priced at £5 each including postage and packing. The BSAENM have also published a textbook Environmental Medicine in Clinical practice at £43 including postage and packing, which includes a lot of information and is available from the address given, or you can order by phone on 01703 812124.

They also publish a quarterly peer-reviewed international journal. The Journal of Nutritional and Environmental Medicine, with features on original research, reviews and reports which are relevant to the clinical practice of nutritional and environmental medicine. It is the official journal of The British Society for Allergy Environmental and Nutritional Medicine, the American Academy of Environmental Medicine and the Australian College of Nutritional and Environmental Medicine. Your GP may like to write for a complimentary copy and a membership application form, to the address given earlier.

'E' for Additives by Maurice Hanssen and Jill Marsden
Published by Thorsons ISBN 0-7225-1562-6

The Food Watch Alternative Cook Book by Honor J Campbell
Published by Ashgrove Press ISBN 1-85398-017-X

The Allergy Hand Book by Dr Keith Mumby
Published by Thorsons ISBN 0-7225-1657-6

Daylight Robbery by Dr Damien Downing
Published by Arrow ISBN 0-09-956740-7

Why M E? by Dr Belinda Dawes and Dr Damien Downing
Published by Grafton ISBN 0-586-20666-3

Candida Albicans (yeast free recipes for renewed good health and vitality) by Richard Turner and Elizabeth Simonsen
Published by Thorsons ISBN 0-7225-1910-9

Recipes for Allergics by Billie Little
Published by Bantam Books ISBN 0-553-17362-6

The Vitamin Fact Finder by Carol Hunter
Published by Thorsons ISBN 0-7225-0932-4

Not All In The Mind by Dr Richard Mackarness
Published by Pan ISBN 0-330-31354-1

The Whole Health Manual by Patrick Holford
Published by Thorsons ISBN 0-7225-1682-7

Food Combining For Health (a new look at the 'Hay' system)
by Doris Grant and Jean Joyce
Published by Thorsons ISBN 0-7225-0882-4

Freedom From Allergy Cook Book by Ronald Greenberg MD and Angela Nori
Published by Blue Poppy Press ISBN 0-96800302-0-3

Encyclopaedia of Allergy and Environmental Illness by
Ellen Rothera
Published by David and Charles ISBN 0-7153-9954-3

The Complete Guide to Food Allergy and Intolerance by
Dr Jonathan Brostoff and Linda Gamlin
Published by Bloomsbury (0989) ISBN 0 7475 1260 4

Allergy A la Carte Single Food Cookery by the Reverend
Elaine Halls
Text, Drawing, Printing and Production by Rev Elaine Halls and
available from her by mail order from:
The Manse, 63 Kingsmark Avenue, Chepstow, NP6 5LY
Tel/Fax 01291 622100 - also available through Airedale Allergy
Centre, Steeton, Near Keighley, West Yorkshire

Beating Cancer With Nutrition by Dr Patrick Quillin and Noreen
Quillin
Published by Nutrition Times Press Inc. ISBN 0-9638372-0-6

Allergy: A Practical Guide to Coping by Dr Jonathan Maberly and
Dr Honor Anthony.
Published by Crowood Press ISBN 1 85223 172 6 available only
through Airedale Allergy Centre, High Hall, Steeton near Keighley,
West Yorkshire.

The Allergy Survival Guide by Jane Houlton
Published by Vermilion ISBN 009 177505 1

Allergies Your Hidden Enemy by Theron Randolph and Ralph
Moss
Published by Thorsons ISBN 0 7225 0981 2

Hayfever The Complete Guide Dr Jonathan Brostoff and Linda
Gamlin
Published by Bloomsbury ISBN 0 7475 1291 4

Yorkshire Guide to Smoke-Free Air, a comprehensive list of places to stay and eat smoke-free, Pubs, Cafes, Hotels, Guest Houses, Coffee Shops and Restaurants, including places with the Roy Castle Good Air Award.
Published by Yorkshire ASH available through Yorkshire ASH, St Mary's Hospital, Leeds LS12 2QE Tel 0113 279 4535 for details.

INDEX

Recipe For Day Two

Recipes for Day Three

Recipes For Day Four

Desserts Day Four

Non-Rotating Section

Cooking Substitutes

Vitamins and Minerals

Minerals

Useful Names and Addresses of Suppliers